PRIMARY MATHEMATICS 5A

Third Edition

Primary Mathematics Project Team

Project Director
Dr Kho Tek Hong

Team Members
Chee Kum Hoong, Hector
Liang Hin Hoon
Lim Eng Tann
Lim Hui Cheng, Rosalind
Ng Hwee Wan
Ng Siew Lee

Curriculum Specialists
Cheong Ngan Peng, Christina
Ho Juan Beng
Sin Kwai Meng

SINGAPOREMATH.COM INC.
19363 WILLAMETTE DR. #237
WEST LINN, OR 97068
www.singaporemath.com

 Curriculum Planning & Development Division
Ministry of Education, Singapore

FEDERAL
PUBLICATIONS
An imprint of Times Media

Published by
Times Media Private Limited
A member of the Times Publishing Group
Times Centre
1 New Industrial Road
Singapore 536196
E-mail: fps@corp.tpl.com.sg
Online Book Store: http://www.timesone.com.sg/fpl

First published   1983
Second Edition 1994
Third Edition   1999
Reprinted   1999, 2000

ISBN 981 01 8051 9

Printed by Times Offset (M) Sdn. Bhd

Illustrator
Danny Goh

ACKNOWLEDGEMENTS

The project team would like to record their thanks to the following:

• members of the Primary Mathematics Team who developed the first edition and second edition of the package

• members of the Steering Committee for the second edition of the package

• teachers who tested the materials in the package and provided useful insights and suggestions

• Educational Technology Division, for the design and production of the audio-visual components of the package

• all those who have helped in one way or another in the development and production of the package

PREFACE

The Primary Mathematics package comprises textbooks, workbooks, teacher's guides and audio-visual materials.

The main feature of the package is the use **Concrete** ➡ **Pictorial** ➡ **Abstract** approach. The pupils are provided with the necessary learning experiences beginning with the concrete and pictorial stages, followed by the abstract stage to enable them to learn mathematics meaningfully. Like the previous editions of the package, this edition encourages active thinking processes, communication of mathematical ideas and problem solving.

This textbook is accompanied by a workbook and a teacher's guide. It comprises 6 units. Each unit is divided into parts: **1**, **2**, . . . Each part starts with a meaningful situation for communication and is followed by specific learning tasks numbered 1, 2, . . . The sign Workbook Exercise⟩ is used to link the textbook to the workbook exercises.

Practice exercises are designed to provide the pupils with further practice after they have done the relevant workbook exercises. Review exercises and revision exercises are provided for cumulative reviews of concepts and skills. All the practice exercises, review exercises and revision exercises are optional exercises. Answers to the practice exercises and review exercises are given at the back of the textbook.

The colour patch ■ is used to invite active participation from the pupils and to facilitate oral discussion. The pupils are advised not to write on the colour patches.

CONTENTS

1 Whole Numbers

1 Place Values

This block is made up of unit cubes.
How many unit cubes are there?

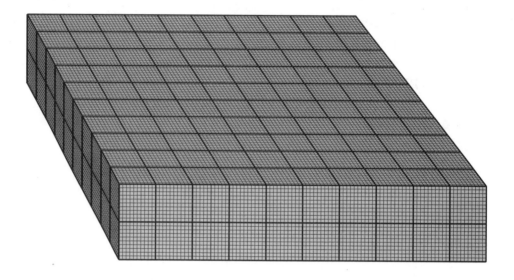

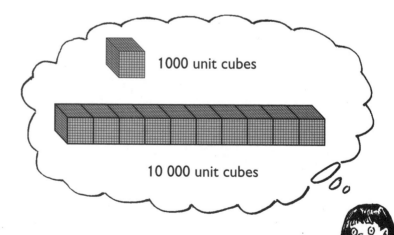

1000 unit cubes

10 000 unit cubes

200 000

two hundred thousand

1. A library has a collection of 124 936 books.

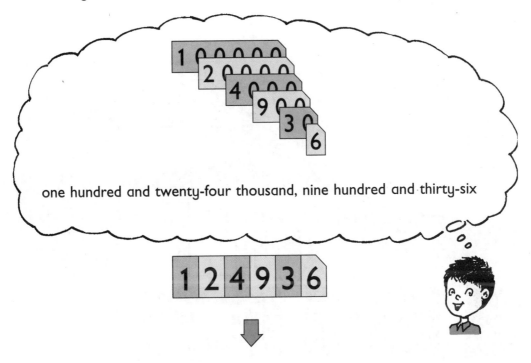

one hundred and twenty-four thousand, nine hundred and thirty-six

Hundred thousands	Ten thousands	Thousands	Hundreds	Tens	Ones
1	2	4	9	3	6

(a) In 124 936, the digit 2 is in the ten thousands place.

Its value is ▪ .

(b) The digit 1 is in the hundred thousands place.
Its value is ▪ .

2. Write the following in words.
   (a) 435 672   (b) 500 500   (c) 404 040
   (d) 345 713   (e) 700 370   (f) 311 012
   (g) 840 382   (h) 600 005   (i) 999 999

3. Write the following in figures.
   (a) Four hundred and one thousand and sixty-two
   (b) Nine hundred and seventy thousand, five hundred and five
   (c) Seven hundred thousand and nine

Workbook Exercise 1

② Millions

The selling price of the house is $2 **million**.
How many one-thousand-dollar notes do you need to buy the house?

1 million = 1000 thousands
2 millions = ▇ thousands

We write $2 million as
$2,000,000.

1. (a) According to the 1980 census, the population of Singapore was about 2,414,000.

We read 2,414,000 as
two million, four hundred and fourteen thousand.

In 2,414,000, the digit ■ is in the millions place.

(b) According to the 1990 census, the population of Singapore has exceeded 3 000 000.

We read
3 000 000
as three million.

In 3 000 000, the digit 3 is in the ■ place.

2. Write the following in words.
   (a) 5 000 000
   (b) 4 126 000
   (c) 3 690 000
   (d) 6 800 000

3. Write the following in figures.
   (a) Six million
   (b) Seven million and three thousand
   (c) Eight million
   (d) Nine million and twenty-three thousand

Workbook Exercise 2

PRACTICE 1A

1. Write the following in figures.
    (a) Eleven thousand and twelve
    (b) One hundred and fifteen thousand and six hundred
    (c) Seven hundred thousand and thirteen
    (d) Eight hundred and eighty thousand and five
    (e) Five million
    (f) Four million and two hundred thousand
    (g) Ten million
    (h) Eight million and eight thousand

2. Write the following in words.
    (a) 207 306   (b) 560 003   (c) 700 000
    (d) 3 450 000   (e) 6 020 000   (f) 4 003 000

3. What is the value of the digit 8 in each of the following?
    (a) 72 **8**45   (b) **8**0 375   (c) 901 9**8**2
    (d) **8**10 034   (e) 9 **6**48 000   (f) **8** 162 000

4. What are the missing numbers?
    (a) 16 500 = 10 000 + ■ + 500
    (b) 225 430 = ■ + 20 000 + 5000 + 400 + 30
    (c) 100 000 + 80 000 + 4000 + 900 = ■
    (d) 7 000 000 + 600 000 + 9000 = ■
    (e) 9 000 000 + 20 000 + 1000 = ■
    (f) 8 532 000 = 8 000 000 + 500 000 + ■ + 2000

5. Complete the following number patterns.
    (a) 42 668, 43 668, ■, ■, 46 668
    (b) 70 500, 71 500, 72 500, ■, ■
    (c) 83 002, 93 002, ■, ■, 123 002
    (d) 5 632 000, 5 642 000, ■, ■, 5 672 000
    (e) 9 742 000, 8 742 000, ■, 6 742 000, ■

6. Arrange the numbers in increasing order.
    (a) 53 760, 53 670, 56 370, 53 607
    (b) 324 468, 342 468, 324 648, 342 486
    (c) 2 537 000, 2 357 000, 3 257 000, 425 700

3 Approximation and Estimation

4865 people watched a badminton match.

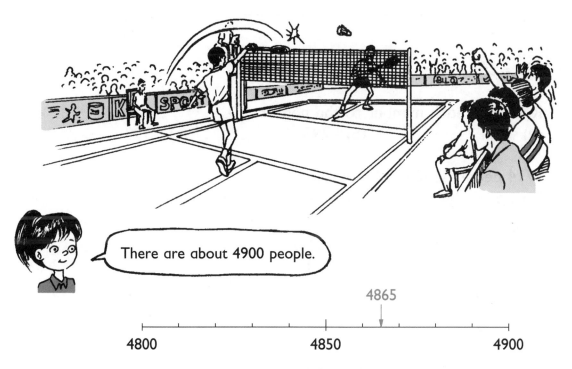

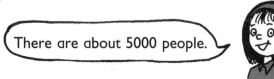

There are about 4900 people.

```
            4865
             ↓
 |-----------|-----------|
4800       4850        4900
```

Sally rounds off 4865 **to the nearest hundred**.

$4865 \approx 4900$

4865 is **approximately** 4900.

There are about 5000 people.

```
                    4865
                     ↓
 |--------|----------|
4000     4500      5000
```

Jenny rounds off 4865 **to the nearest thousand**.

$4865 \approx 5000$

4865 is **approximately** 5000.

1. There are **487** pages in a book.
   Round off the number of pages to the nearest ten.

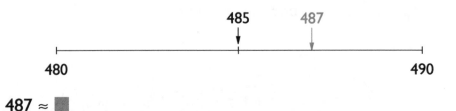

   487 ≈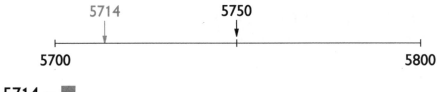

2. Round off each number to the nearest 10.
   (a) **604**   (b) **795**   (c) **999**

3. **5714** people visited a book fair.
   Round off the number of visitors to the nearest hundred.

   5714 ≈ ■

4. Round off each number to the nearest 100.
   (a) **3650**   (b) **6047**   (c) **4995**

5. Round off **16 500** to the nearest thousand.

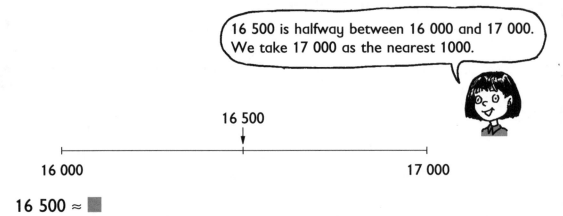

   16 500 is halfway between 16 000 and 17 000.
   We take 17 000 as the nearest 1000.

   16 500 ≈ ■

6. Round off each number to the nearest 1000.
   (a) **23 490**   (b) **54 550**   (c) **39 900**

Workbook Exercise 3

To round off a number to the nearest thousand, we look at the digit in the hundreds place. If it is 5 or greater than 5, we round up; if it is smaller than 5, we round down.

7. Round off each number to the nearest 1000.
   (a) 49 287 ≈ 49 000
   (b) 73 501 ≈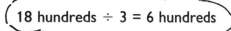
   (c) 804 390 ≈ ■
   (d) 129 500 ≈ ■

8. Find the value of 1800 ÷ 3.

   1800 ÷ 3 = ■

   18 hundreds ÷ 3 = 6 hundreds

9. Find the value of
   (a) 27 000 + 6000
   (b) 45 000 − 8000
   (c) 7000 × 4
   (d) 3500 ÷ 5

10. Estimate the value of 2934 × 6.

    2934 × 6 ≈ 3000 × 6

    = ■

11. Estimate the value of 5423 ÷ 8.

    5423 ÷ 8 ≈ 5600 ÷ 8

    = ■

    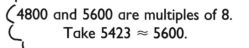

    4800 and 5600 are multiples of 8.
    Take 5423 ≈ 5600.

12. Estimate the value of
    (a) 6390 + 5992
    (b) 78 123 + 8969
    (c) 8307 − 4265
    (d) 45 627 − 7324
    (e) 3806 × 9
    (f) 9794 × 5
    (g) 4785 ÷ 6
    (h) 3782 ÷ 4

Workbook Exercise 4

PRACTICE 1B

1. Round off each number to the nearest 10.
    (a) 72   (b) 655   (c) 1289

2. Round off each number to the nearest 100.
    (a) 342   (b) 1259   (c) 20 753

3. Round off each number to the nearest 1000.
    (a) 6850   (b) 10 500   (c) 125 498

4. David bought a television set for $849.
    Round off this amount to the nearest hundred dollars.

5. Mr Raju bought a car for $69 500.
    Round off this amount to the nearest thousand dollars.

6. A spaceship travelled 999 540 km.
    Round off this distance to the nearest 1000 km.

7. This table shows the number of people living in three towns.

    (a) Round off the number of
         people in each town to
         the nearest 1000.

Number of people
Town A : 179 920
Town B : 176 392
Town C : 170 500

    (b) Use your answers in part (a)
         to estimate the total number of
         people in the 3 towns.

8. Round each number to the nearest 1000.
    Then estimate the value of
    (a) 32 370 + 4959   (b) 24 890 + 5016
    (c) 48 207 − 9864   (d) 54 500 − 6892

9. Estimate the value of
    (a) 8659×4 (b) 6023×9
    (c) $7080 \div 8$ (d) $4378 \div 7$

4 Multiplying by Tens, Hundreds or Thousands

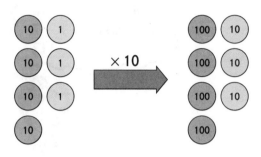

$$43 \times 10 = 430$$

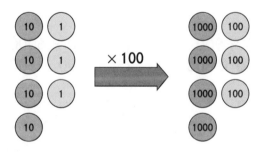

$$43 \times 100 = 4300$$

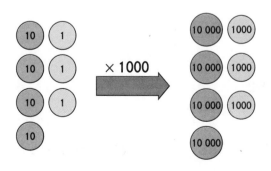

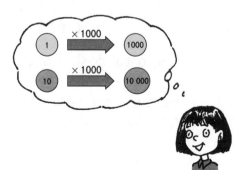

$$43 \times 1000 = 43\ 000$$

1. Multiply.
   (a) 328×10 (b) 100×536 (c) 63×1000

2. Multiply 16 by 70.

   $16 \times 70 = 16 \times 7 \times 10$

   $\qquad = 112 \times 10$

   $\qquad = 1120$

   Multiply 16 by 7 first.

   $\begin{array}{r} 16 \\ \times\ 7 \\ \hline 112 \end{array}$

3. Multiply 48 by 3.
   Then find the value of
   (a) 48×30 (b) 48×300 (c) 48×3000

4. Multiply 450 by 6.
   Then find the value of
   (a) 450×60 (b) 450×600 (c) 450×6000

5. Multiply.
   (a) 200×500 (b) 600×900 (c) 800×6000
   (d) 500×2000 (e) 4000×600 (f) 2000×5000

6. Estimate the value of 702×19.

   $702 \times 19 \approx 700 \times 20$

   $\qquad = \blacksquare$

   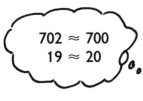

   $702 \approx 700$
   $19 \approx 20$

7. Mrs. Chen needs 543 costumes for the pupils to take part in a parade. Each costume costs \$35. Give a quick estimate of the total cost of the costumes.

   $35 \times 543 \approx 40 \times 500$
   $\qquad = 20\ 000$

   The total cost is about \$20 **000**.

8. Estimate the value of
   (a) 529×34 (b) 75×386 (c) 7804×59

Workbook Exercise 5

5 Dividing by Tens, Hundreds or Thousands

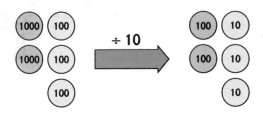

$$2300 \div 10 = 230$$

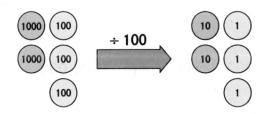

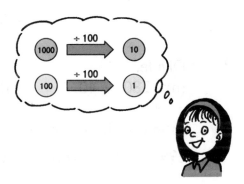

$$2300 \div 100 = 23$$

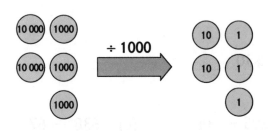

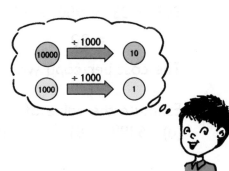

$$23\ 000 \div 1000 = 23$$

1. Divide.
   (a) $520 \div 10$ (b) $7400 \div 100$ (c) $40\,000 \div 1000$

2. (a) Divide 15 000 by 30.

   $$15\,000 \div 30 = 15\,000 \div 10 \div 3$$
   $$= 1500 \div 3$$
   $$= 500$$

   (b) Divide 15 000 by 300.

   $$15\,000 \div 300 = 15\,000 \div 100 \div 3$$
   $$= 150 \div 3$$
   $$= 50$$

   (c) Divide 15 000 by 3000.

   $$15\,000 \div 3000 = 15\,000 \div 1000 \div 3$$
   $$= 15 \div 3$$
   $$= 5$$

3. Divide.
   (a) $280 \div 40$ (b) $64\,000 \div 800$ (c) $200\,000 \div 5000$

4. Estimate the value of $2992 \div 38$.

   $$2992 \div 38 \approx 2800 \div 40$$
   $$= \blacksquare$$

5. Mr. Li paid $959 for 33 copies of a software. Give a quick estimate of the cost per copy.

   $$959 \div 33 \approx 900 \div 30$$
   $$= 30$$

   The cost per copy was about $30.

6. Estimate the value of
   (a) $6398 \div 81$ (b) $2205 \div 34$ (c) $638 \div 67$

Workbook Exercise 6

6 Order of Operations

Minghua arranges his stamps on two pages of his stamp album like this:

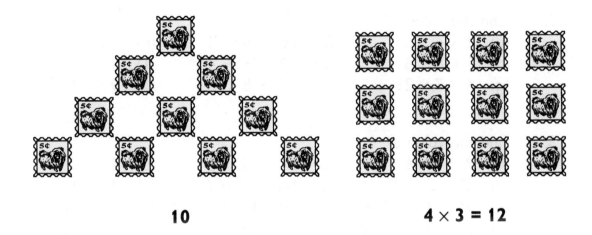

10   4 × 3 = 12

Then he finds the total number of stamps.

Do multiplication first.

$$10 + 4 \times 3 = 10 + 12$$
$$= 22$$

There are 22 stamps altogether.

Order of Operations:

Do multiplication and division before addition and subtraction.

1. Find the value of
   (a) $12 + 8 - 10$
   (b) $60 - 12 - 24$
   (c) $31 - 19 + 11$
   (d) $43 + 16 - 27$
   (e) $64 + 26 + 57$
   (f) $90 - 12 + 21$
   (g) $55 + 69 - 25$
   (h) $111 - 89 - 11$
   (i) $58 - 25 + 42$

2. Find the value of
   (a) $2 \times 4 \times 8$
   (b) $60 \div 4 \div 3$
   (c) $54 \div 6 \times 3$
   (d) $9 \times 8 \times 6$
   (e) $72 \div 6 \div 4$
   (f) $4 \times 24 \div 8$
   (g) $4 \times 7 \times 25$
   (h) $64 \div 8 \div 8$
   (i) $9 \times 81 \div 9$

3. Find the value of
   (a) $9 + 3 \times 6$
   (b) $27 - 12 \div 3$
   (c) $4 + 15 \times 12$
   (d) $80 - 5 \times 10$
   (e) $54 - 48 \div 6$
   (f) $9 + 81 \div 9$
   (g) $56 - 8 \times 5 + 4$
   (h) $70 + 80 \div 5 \times 4$
   (i) $96 \div 8 - 6 \times 2$
   (j) $6 + 54 \div 9 \times 2$
   (k) $49 - 45 \div 5 \times 3$
   (l) $62 + 42 \div 7 - 6$

   > Workbook Exercise 7

4. Find the value of $27 - 2 \times (3 + 5)$.

   $$27 - 2 \times (\mathbf{3 + 5})$$
   $$= 27 - 2 \times \mathbf{8}$$
   $$= \blacksquare$$

   Do what is in the **brackets** first.

5. Find the value of
   (a) $76 + (36 + 164)$
   (b) $200 - (87 - 13)$
   (c) $99 - (87 + 12)$
   (d) $18 \times (5 \times 2)$
   (e) $490 \div (7 \times 7)$
   (f) $153 \times (27 \div 9)$

6. Find the value of
   (a) $60 \div (4 + 8)$
   (b) $20 - 2 \times (18 \div 6)$
   (c) $25 + (5 + 7) \div 3$
   (d) $(22 + 10) \div 8 \times 5$
   (e) $(50 - 42) \div 2 \times 7$
   (f) $100 \div 10 \times (4 + 6)$

   > Workbook Exercise 8

20

PRACTICE 1C

1. Multiply.
   (a) 238×10
   (b) 700×100
   (c) 37×1000
   (d) 10×400
   (e) 100×280
   (f) 1000×520

2. Multiply 56 by 7.
   Then find the value of
   (a) 56×70
   (b) 56×700
   (c) 56×7000

3. Multiply 75 by 9.
   Then find the value of
   (a) 75×90
   (b) 75×900
   (c) 75×9000

4. Divide 72 by 8.
   Then find the value of
   (a) $720\,000 \div 80$
   (b) $720\,000 \div 800$
   (c) $720\,000 \div 8000$

5. Divide 900 by 6.
   Then find the value of
   (a) $90\,000 \div 60$
   (b) $90\,000 \div 600$
   (c) $90\,000 \div 6000$

6. Divide.
   (a) $360 \div 90$
   (b) $7600 \div 40$
   (c) $90\,600 \div 600$
   (d) $4080 \div 80$
   (e) $350\,000 \div 500$
   (f) $412\,000 \div 4000$

7. Find the value of
   (a) $48 - 17 + 25$
   (b) $6 \times 5 \times 10$
   (c) $81 \div 9 \div 3$
   (d) $50 \div 5 + 5$
   (e) $64 - 3 \times 9$
   (f) $72 - 36 \div 9$
   (g) $27 + 15 \div 3 \times 2$
   (h) $40 \div 2 - 2 \times 5$
   (i) $10 + 24 \div 8 + 8$
   (j) $(38 - 17) \div 3 \times 10$
   (k) $35 \div (10 - 3) \times 10$
   (l) $(13 + 7) \div (9 - 4)$

8. Find the value of
   (a) $372 - (45 - 29)$
   (b) $372 - 45 + 29$
   (c) $372 - 45 - 29$
   (d) $372 - (45 + 29)$
   (e) $128 \div 4 \div 2$
   (f) $128 \div (4 \times 2)$
   (g) $128 \div 4 \times 2$
   (h) $126 \div (4 \div 2)$

Word Problems

Mrs Li bought 420 mangoes for $378. She packed the mangoes in packets of 4 mangoes each and sold all the mangoes at $6 per packet. How much money did she make?

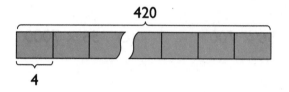

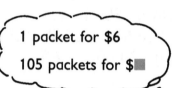

4 mangoes in 1 packet.

420 mangoes in ■ packets

$420 \div 4 = 105$

There were 105 packets of mangoes.

1 packet for $6

105 packets for $■

$\$6 \times 105 = \$630$

Mrs Li sold the mangoes for $630.

Selling price – Cost price = ■

$\$630 - \$378 = \$■$

Mrs Li made $■.

1. Raju and Samy shared **$410** between them. Raju received **$100** more than Samy. How much money did Samy receive?

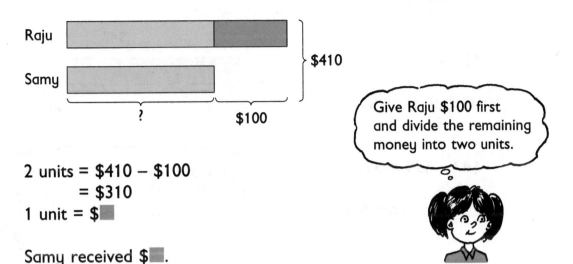

Raju

Samy

$410

?

$100

Give Raju $100 first and divide the remaining money into two units.

2 units = $410 − $100
　　　 = $310
1 unit = $▇

Samy received $▇.

2. Peter collected a total of 1170 stamps. He collected 4 times as many Singapore stamps as foreign stamps. How many Singapore stamps did he collect?

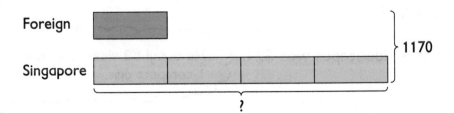

Foreign

Singapore

1170

?

Workbook Exercise 9

3. Mr Gopal bought 2 similar T-shirts and a belt. He paid $50 to the cashier and received $3 change. If the belt cost $29, find the cost of each T-shirt.

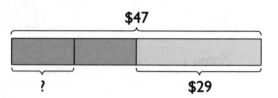

$50 – $3 = $47

Mr Gopal spent $47.

$47 – $29 = $18

The T-shirts cost $18.

> The total cost of 2 T-shirts and 1 belt is $47.

$18 ÷ 2 = $■

The cost of each T-shirt was $■.

4. Henry bought a compact disc and 3 videotapes. The compact disc cost $16. If a compact disc cost twice as much as a videotape, how much did he spend altogether?

$16 ÷ 2 = $8   CD

A videotape cost $8.   Tape

$8 × 3 = $24

The cost of 3 videotapes was $24.

> He bought 3 videotapes and 1 compact disc.

$24 + $16 = $■

He spent $■ altogether.

Workbook Exercise 10

24

PRACTICE 1D

1. John is 15 kg heavier than Peter. Their total weight is 127 kg. Find John's weight.

2. There are 3 times as many boys as girls. If there are 24 more boys than girls, how many children are there altogether?

3. The total weight of Peter, David and Henry is 123 kg. Peter is 15 kg heavier than David. David is 3 kg lighter than Henry. Find Henry's weight.

4. Ahmad has $180 and Raju has $150. How much money must Ahmad give Raju so that they each will have an equal amount of money?

5. Minghui has twice as many stickers as David. How many stickers must Minghui give David so that they each will have 120 stickers?

6. Peter has twice as many stickers as Ali. Ali has 40 more stickers than Lihua. They have 300 stickers altogether. How many stickers does Peter have?

7. At a book fair, Ali bought 24 books at 3 for $5 and had $2 left. How much money did he have at first?

8. Raju bought 3 books and a magazine. He paid $30 to the cashier and received $5 change. If the magazine cost twice as much as each book, find the cost of the magazine.

9. Mr Li bought 155 oranges for $35. He found that 15 of them were rotten. He sold all the remaining oranges at 7 for $2. How much money did he make?

10. John and Paul spent $45 altogether. John and Henry spent $65 altogether. If Henry spent 3 times as much as Paul, how much did John spend?

2 Multiplication and Division by a 2-digit Whole Number

1 Multiplication

(a)   Multiply 78 by 30.

Method 1:

$$78 \times 30 = 78 \times 3 \times 10$$
$$= 234 \times 10$$
$$= 2340$$

Multiply 78 by 3 first.

$$\begin{array}{r} 78 \\ \times\ 3 \\ \hline 234 \end{array}$$

Method 2:

$$\begin{array}{r} 78 \\ \times\ 30 \\ \hline 2340 \end{array}$$

(b)   Multiply 650 by 40.

$$\begin{array}{r} 650 \\ \times\ 40 \\ \hline 26000 \end{array}$$

1. Multiply.

(a)
$$\begin{array}{r} 53 \\ \times\ 60 \\ \hline \end{array}$$

(b)
$$\begin{array}{r} 247 \\ \times\ 80 \\ \hline \end{array}$$

2. Multiply.

(a) 58×80 (b) 46×50 (c) 27×90

(d) 207×60 (e) 739×40 (f) 641×70

3. Multiply.

(a)
$$\begin{array}{rl} 24 & \\ \times\ 13 & \\ \hline 72 & \leftarrow 24 \times 3 \\ 240 & \leftarrow 24 \times 10 \\ \hline 312 & \end{array}$$

(b)
$$\begin{array}{r} 52 \\ \times\ 47 \\ \hline \end{array}$$

(c)
$$\begin{array}{rl} 325 & \\ \times\ 54 & \\ \hline 1300 & \leftarrow 325 \times 4 \\ 16250 & \leftarrow 325 \times 50 \\ \hline \end{array}$$

(d)
$$\begin{array}{r} 618 \\ \times\ 72 \\ \hline \end{array}$$

4. Multiply.

(a) 67×44 (b) 53×48 (c) 29×96

(d) 236×82 (e) 457×35 (f) 606×47

5. Multiply.

(a)
$$\begin{array}{r} 4635 \\ \times\ 26 \\ \hline \end{array}$$

(b)
$$\begin{array}{r} 8247 \\ \times\ 38 \\ \hline \end{array}$$

6. Multiply.

(a) 3059×53 (b) 7105×62 (c) 2537×48

(d) 3860×69 (e) 6394×57 (f) 5482×74

Workbook Exercise 11

② Division

(a) Divide 140 by 20.

Method 1:

$$140 \div 20 = 7$$

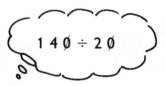

Method 2:

```
      7
20)140
   140
     0
```

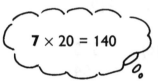

(b) Divide 150 by 20.

```
      7
20)150
   140
    10
```

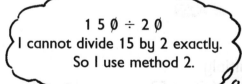

28

1. Divide.

(a)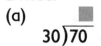
$$30\overline{)70}$$

(b)
$$60\overline{)430}$$

(c)
$$20\overline{)89}$$

(d)
$$70\overline{)625}$$

2. Divide.

(a) $90 \div 50$ (b) $79 \div 40$ (c) $85 \div 30$

(d) $540 \div 70$ (e) $613 \div 90$ (f) $438 \div 60$

3. Divide 74 by 21.

$$\begin{array}{r} 3 \\ 21\overline{)74} \\ 63 \\ \hline 11 \end{array}$$

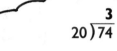

$$\begin{array}{r} 3 \\ 20\overline{)74} \end{array}$$

The estimated quotient is 3.

4. Divide 256 by 47.

$$\begin{array}{r} 5 \\ 47\overline{)256} \\ 235 \\ \hline 21 \end{array}$$

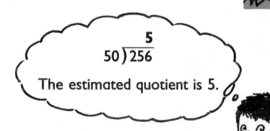

$$\begin{array}{r} 5 \\ 50\overline{)256} \end{array}$$

The estimated quotient is 5.

5. Divide.

(a) $63 \div 17$ (b) $48 \div 23$ (c) $85 \div 38$

(d) $76 \div 34$ (e) $94 \div 43$ (f) $57 \div 29$

(g) $149 \div 67$ (h) $509 \div 84$ (i) $756 \div 95$

(j) $668 \div 72$ (k) $279 \div 56$ (l) $183 \div 44$

6. Divide 89 by 24.

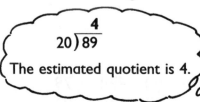

$$\begin{array}{r} 4 \\ 20\overline{)89} \end{array}$$

The estimated quotient is 4.

$$\begin{array}{r} 4 \\ 24\overline{)89} \\ 96 \\ \hline \end{array}$$

$$\begin{array}{r} 3 \\ 24\overline{)89} \\ 72 \\ \hline 17 \end{array}$$

The estimated quotient
is too big. Try 3.

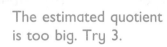

29

7. Divide 78 by 26.

The estimated quotient is 2.

$$26\overline{)78} \atop \begin{array}{r} 2 \\ 52 \\ \hline 26 \end{array}$$

The estimated quotient is too small. Try 3.

$$26\overline{)78} \atop \begin{array}{r} 3 \\ 78 \\ \hline 0 \end{array}$$

8. Divide.
   (a) 68 ÷ 17
   (d) 83 ÷ 21

   (b) 77 ÷ 25
   (e) 84 ÷ 43

   (c) 94 ÷ 33
   (f) 75 ÷ 15

9. Divide 285 by 33.

The estimated quotient is 9.

$$33\overline{)285} \atop \begin{array}{r} 9 \\ 297 \end{array}$$

The estimated quotient is too big. Try 8.

$$33\overline{)285} \atop \begin{array}{r} 8 \\ 264 \\ \hline 21 \end{array}$$

10. Divide 473 by 78.

The estimated quotient is 5.

$$78\overline{)473} \atop \begin{array}{r} 5 \\ 390 \\ \hline 83 \end{array}$$

The estimated quotient is too small. Try 6.

$$78\overline{)473} \atop \begin{array}{r} 6 \\ 468 \\ \hline 5 \end{array}$$

11. Divide.
    (a) 207 ÷ 23
    (d) 572 ÷ 64

    (b) 236 ÷ 39
    (e) 464 ÷ 58

    (c) 474 ÷ 79
    (f) 640 ÷ 93

Workbook Exercise 12

12. Divide 570 by 16.

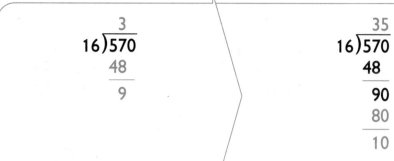

Divide 57 tens by 16.   Divide 90 by 16.

13. Divide.

(a)
```
        25
   34 ) 870
        68
       ────
        190
        170
       ────
         20
```

(b)
```
        30
   28 ) 862
        84
       ────
         22
```

(c)
```
         ■
   47 ) 703
```

(d)
```
         ■
   15 ) 612
```

14. Divide.

(a) 552 ÷ 24   (b) 660 ÷ 29   (c) 925 ÷ 46
(d) 399 ÷ 31   (e) 708 ÷ 67   (f) 374 ÷ 18

15. Divide.

(a)
```
        234
   28 ) 6552
        56
       ─────
         95
         84
       ─────
        112
        112
       ─────
          0
```

(b)
```
         83
   52 ) 4328
        416
       ─────
        168
        156
       ─────
         12
```

(c)
```
          ■
   64 ) 6820
```

(d)
```
          ■
   45 ) 3185
```

16. Divide.

(a) 6692 ÷ 28   (b) 2409 ÷ 18   (c) 1495 ÷ 45
(d) 6008 ÷ 56   (e) 1054 ÷ 37   (f) 9864 ÷ 29

Workbook Exercise 13

PRACTICE 2A

Multiply.

	(a)	(b)	(c)
1.	407×84	690×49	941×73
2.	5395×51	7404×85	3092×63

Divide.

	(a)	(b)	(c)
3.	$89 \div 24$	$92 \div 33$	$56 \div 18$
4.	$848 \div 16$	$403 \div 67$	$505 \div 53$
5.	$722 \div 38$	$895 \div 23$	$999 \div 42$
6.	$7684 \div 78$	$1340 \div 23$	$9670 \div 54$

7. A baker uses 12 eggs to bake a cake.
   How many eggs does he need if he wants to bake 36 cakes?

8. Mr Chen has to drive to Malacca which is 240 km from Singapore. If his car can travel 15 km on 1 litre of petrol, how many litres of petrol does he need for the trip?

9. 1064 balloons were shared equally among 38 pupils. How many balloons did each pupil receive?

10. Cik Fatimah sold 96 tarts at a food fair. The tarts were sold in jars of 12 tarts each. She sold all the tarts at $7 per jar. How much money did she receive?

11. Mr Samy buys a car and pays by instalments. Each instalment is $827. If he still has to pay $280 after paying 72 instalments, how much does the car cost?

12. Miss Lin sold 2034 concert tickets at $16 per ticket. She also sold 840 programmes at $3 each. How much money did she collect altogether?

13. 70 pupils were divided into 14 teams. In each team there were 2 girls. How many boys were there altogether?

14. Mrs Lin baked 840 biscuits. She sold them in packets of 24 biscuits each. How much money did she receive if the selling price per packet was $3?

3 Fractions

1 Fraction and Division

4 children share 3 pancakes equally.
Each child receives 3 quarters.

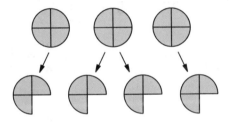

$$3 \div 4 = \frac{3}{4}$$

4 children share 5 pancakes equally.
Each child receives 5 quarters.

$$5 \div 4 = \frac{5}{4}$$

Here is another way to show that $5 \div 4 = \frac{5}{4}$.

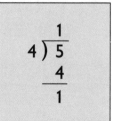

Each child receives 1 pancake first.
Share the remaining pancake.

$$1 \div 4 = \frac{1}{4}$$

Each child receives 1 and $\frac{1}{4}$ pancakes.

$$5 \div 4 = 1\frac{1}{4}$$

$$= \frac{4}{4} + \frac{1}{4}$$

$$= \frac{5}{4}$$

1. Express $\frac{11}{4}$ as a mixed number.

Method 1:

$$\frac{11}{4} = \frac{8}{4} + \frac{3}{4}$$

$$= 2\frac{3}{4}$$

Method 2:

$$\frac{11}{4} = 11 \div 4 = \blacksquare$$

$$\begin{array}{r} 2 \\ 4{\overline{\smash{\big)}\,11}} \\ \underline{8} \\ 3 \end{array}$$

2. A pail contains 8 litres of water. If the water is poured equally into 3 jugs, how much water is there in each jug?

$$8 \div 3 = \blacksquare$$

$$\begin{array}{r} 2 \\ 3\overline{)8} \\ \underline{6} \\ 3 \end{array}$$

There are ■ litres of water in each jug.

3. Find the value of $22 \div 8$.

Method 1:

$$22 \div 8 = 2\frac{6}{8}$$

$$= 2\frac{\blacksquare}{4}$$

$$\begin{array}{r} 2 \\ 8\overline{)22} \\ \underline{16} \\ 6 \end{array}$$

Method 2:

$$22 \div 8 = \frac{22}{8}$$

$$= \frac{\blacksquare}{4}$$

$$= \blacksquare$$

4. Find the value of
   (a) $7 \div 3$ (b) $14 \div 5$ (c) $21 \div 6$ (d) $77 \div 9$

Workbook Exercise 14

PRACTICE 3A

1. Express each of the following as a whole number or a mixed number in its simplest form.

   (a) $\dfrac{13}{5}$ (b) $\dfrac{21}{3}$ (c) $\dfrac{24}{9}$ (d) $\dfrac{50}{6}$

2. Express each of the following answers as a mixed number in its simplest form.

   (a) $30 \div 8$ (b) $21 \div 4$ (c) $35 \div 10$ (d) $78 \div 7$

3. Nancy cut a ribbon into 8 equal pieces. If the ribbon was 26 m long, how many metres long was each piece?

4. Mrs Wang bought 3 m of cloth. She used the cloth to make 9 pillow cases of the same size. How much cloth in metres did she use for each pillow case?

5. Mary baked 10 cakes of the same size. She divided the cakes into 4 equal shares. How many cakes were there in each share?

6. Peter poured 2 litres of milk equally into 5 jugs. How much milk was there in each jug?

7. A red ribbon 11 metres long is 5 times as long as a blue ribbon. How long is the blue ribbon?

8. A tin of biscuits weighing 4 kilograms was divided into 6 equal shares. What was the weight of each share in kilograms?

2 Addition and Subtraction of Unlike Fractions

Ann ate $\frac{1}{3}$ of a cake.

Her brother ate $\frac{1}{2}$ of the same cake.

What fraction of the cake did they eat altogether?

$$\frac{1}{3} + \frac{1}{2} = \frac{2}{6} + \frac{3}{6}$$

$$= \blacksquare$$

The cake is divided into 6 equal parts.
Ann ate 2 parts and her brother ate 3 parts.

They ate ■ of the cake altogether.

$\frac{1}{3}$ and $\frac{1}{2}$ do not have the same denominator.

They are called **unlike fractions**.

$\frac{2}{6}$ and $\frac{3}{6}$ have the same denominator.

They are called **like fractions**.

We can change unlike fractions to like fractions using equivalent fractions:

$$\frac{1}{3}, \frac{2}{6}, \ldots$$

$$\frac{1}{2}, \frac{3}{6}, \ldots$$

1. Add $\dfrac{3}{8}$ and $\dfrac{1}{6}$.

$$\dfrac{3}{8} + \dfrac{1}{6} = \dfrac{\blacksquare}{24} + \dfrac{\blacksquare}{24}$$

$$= \dfrac{\blacksquare}{24}$$

$\dfrac{3}{8}, \dfrac{\blacksquare}{16}, \dfrac{\blacksquare}{24}, \ldots$

$\dfrac{1}{6}, \ldots$

24 is a multiple of 8.
It is also a multiple of 6.

2. Add $\dfrac{2}{3}$ and $\dfrac{2}{5}$.

$$\dfrac{2}{3} + \dfrac{2}{5} = \dfrac{\blacksquare}{15} + \dfrac{\blacksquare}{15}$$

$$= \dfrac{\blacksquare}{15}$$

$$= \blacksquare$$

$\dfrac{2}{5}, \dfrac{\blacksquare}{10}, \dfrac{\blacksquare}{15}, \ldots$

$\dfrac{2}{3}, \ldots$

15 is a common
multiple of 5 and 3.

3. Add $\dfrac{7}{10}$ and $\dfrac{5}{6}$.

$$\dfrac{7}{10} + \dfrac{5}{6} = \dfrac{\blacksquare}{30} + \dfrac{\blacksquare}{30}$$

$$= \dfrac{\blacksquare}{30}$$

$$= \dfrac{\blacksquare}{15}$$

$$= \blacksquare$$

$\dfrac{7}{10}, \dfrac{\blacksquare}{20}, \dfrac{\blacksquare}{30}, \ldots$

$\dfrac{5}{6}, \ldots$

30 is a common
multiple of 10 and 6.

4. Add. Give each answer in its simplest form.

(a) $\dfrac{7}{9} + \dfrac{5}{6}$ (b) $\dfrac{3}{4} + \dfrac{5}{12}$ (c) $\dfrac{3}{10} + \dfrac{5}{6}$

Workbook Exercise 15

5.　Subtract $\frac{1}{6}$ from $\frac{7}{8}$.

$$\frac{7}{8} - \frac{1}{6} = \frac{\blacksquare}{24} - \frac{\blacksquare}{24}$$

$$= \frac{\blacksquare}{24}$$

$\frac{7}{8}, \frac{\blacksquare}{16}, \frac{\blacksquare}{24}, \ldots$

$\frac{1}{6}, \ldots$

24 is a common multiple of 8 and 6.

6.　Subtract $\frac{1}{10}$ from $\frac{5}{6}$.

$$\frac{5}{6} - \frac{1}{10} = \frac{\blacksquare}{30} - \frac{\blacksquare}{30}$$

$$= \frac{\blacksquare}{30}$$

$$= \frac{\blacksquare}{15}$$

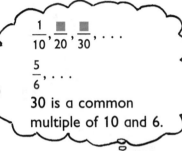

$\frac{1}{10}, \frac{\blacksquare}{20}, \frac{\blacksquare}{30}, \ldots$

$\frac{5}{6}, \ldots$

30 is a common multiple of 10 and 6.

7.　Subtract $\frac{5}{6}$ from $1\frac{7}{10}$.

$$1\frac{7}{10} - \frac{5}{6} = \frac{\blacksquare}{30} - \frac{\blacksquare}{30}$$

$$= \frac{\blacksquare}{30} - \frac{\blacksquare}{30}$$

$$= \frac{\blacksquare}{15}$$

$\frac{7}{10}, \frac{\blacksquare}{20}, \frac{\blacksquare}{30}, \ldots$

$\frac{5}{6}, \ldots$

30 is a common multiple of 10 and 6.

8.　Subtract. Give each answer in its simplest form.

(a)　$\frac{5}{6} - \frac{3}{10}$　　　　(b)　$1\frac{2}{3} - \frac{11}{12}$　　　　(c)　$1\frac{1}{10} - \frac{5}{6}$

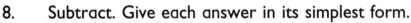

Workbook Exercise 16

PRACTICE 3B

Add or subtract. Give each answer in its simplest form.

	(a)	(b)	(c)
1.	$\dfrac{7}{12} + \dfrac{5}{6}$	$\dfrac{9}{10} + \dfrac{1}{6}$	$\dfrac{5}{6} + \dfrac{7}{8}$
2.	$\dfrac{2}{3} - \dfrac{5}{12}$	$\dfrac{5}{6} - \dfrac{7}{10}$	$\dfrac{3}{4} - \dfrac{1}{6}$
3.	$\dfrac{1}{6} + \dfrac{3}{10}$	$\dfrac{2}{3} + \dfrac{1}{12}$	$\dfrac{5}{12} + \dfrac{1}{8}$
4.	$1\dfrac{3}{8} - \dfrac{7}{12}$	$1\dfrac{1}{3} - \dfrac{7}{10}$	$1\dfrac{3}{10} - \dfrac{5}{6}$

5. John mowed $\dfrac{2}{5}$ of a lawn. His brother mowed $\dfrac{1}{4}$ of it. What fraction of the lawn did they mow?

6. Samy took $\dfrac{3}{4}$ hour to travel from home to the zoo. He took $1\dfrac{1}{4}$ hours to return home. How much longer did he take to return home than to go to the zoo?

7. Mary ate $\dfrac{1}{8}$ of a cake. Peter ate another $\dfrac{1}{4}$ of it.
   (a) What fraction of the cake did they eat altogether?
   (b) What fraction of the cake did Peter eat more than Mary?

8. Ali went to a bookshop. He spent $\dfrac{3}{5}$ of his money on books and $\dfrac{1}{4}$ of it on a pen.
   (a) What fraction of his money did he spend altogether?
   (b) What fraction of his money had he left?

3 Addition and Subtraction of Mixed Numbers

$3\frac{5}{8}$ m

$1\frac{7}{12}$ m

(a) Find the total length of $3\frac{5}{8}$ m and $1\frac{7}{12}$ m.

$$3\frac{5}{8} + 1\frac{7}{12} = 4\frac{5}{8} + \frac{7}{12}$$

$$= 4\frac{15}{24} + \frac{14}{24}$$

$$= 4\frac{\blacksquare}{24}$$

$$= \blacksquare$$

The total length is ■ m.

(b) Add $4\frac{7}{12}$ and $1\frac{3}{4}$.

$$4\frac{7}{12} + 1\frac{3}{4} = 5\frac{7}{12} + \frac{3}{4}$$

$$= 5\frac{7}{12} + \frac{9}{12}$$

$$= 5\frac{\blacksquare}{12}$$

$$= 5\frac{\blacksquare}{3}$$

$$= \blacksquare$$

Express the answer in its simplest form.

1. Add $3\frac{1}{6}$ and $1\frac{9}{10}$.

$$3\frac{1}{6} + 1\frac{9}{10} = 4\frac{1}{6} + \frac{9}{10}$$

$$= 4\frac{\blacksquare}{30} + \frac{\blacksquare}{30}$$

$$= 4\frac{\blacksquare}{30}$$

$$= \blacksquare$$

Workbook Exercise 17

2. Find the difference in length between $4\frac{3}{4}$ m and $3\frac{7}{12}$ m.

$$4\frac{3}{4} - 3\frac{7}{12} = 1\frac{3}{4} - \frac{7}{12}$$

$$= 1\frac{9}{12} - \frac{7}{12}$$

$$= 1\frac{\blacksquare}{12}$$

$$= \blacksquare$$

$4\frac{3}{4} \xrightarrow{-1} \blacksquare \xrightarrow{-\frac{7}{12}} \blacksquare$

The difference in length is $\blacksquare$ m.

3. Subtract.

(a) $3\frac{1}{6} - 1\frac{5}{9} = 2\frac{1}{6} - \frac{5}{9}$

$$= 2\frac{3}{18} - \frac{10}{18}$$

$$= 1\frac{\blacksquare}{18} - \frac{10}{18}$$

$$= \blacksquare$$

(b) $4\frac{1}{6} - 1\frac{3}{10} = 3\frac{1}{6} - \frac{3}{10}$

$$= 3\frac{\blacksquare}{30} - \frac{9}{30}$$

$$= 2\frac{\blacksquare}{30} - \frac{9}{30}$$

$$= 2\frac{\blacksquare}{30} = \blacksquare$$

$$= \blacksquare$$

Workbook Exercise 18

PRACTICE 3C

Add or subtract. Give each answer in its simplest form.

	(a)	(b)	(c)
1.	$2\frac{2}{3} + 1\frac{5}{9}$	$2\frac{1}{8} + 1\frac{5}{6}$	$1\frac{1}{4} + 2\frac{5}{6}$
2.	$3\frac{5}{6} - 1\frac{1}{3}$	$3\frac{4}{5} - 1\frac{3}{10}$	$4\frac{5}{6} - 1\frac{1}{4}$
3.	$3\frac{2}{9} + 1\frac{1}{6}$	$2\frac{5}{6} + 5\frac{1}{2}$	$2\frac{5}{6} + 1\frac{3}{8}$
4.	$4\frac{1}{6} - 1\frac{2}{3}$	$3\frac{1}{6} - 2\frac{1}{10}$	$3\frac{3}{10} - 1\frac{1}{6}$

5. Robert jogged $1\frac{2}{5}$ km. His brother jogged $2\frac{1}{2}$ km. Who jogged a longer distance? How much longer?

6. There were $3\frac{1}{6}$ cakes on the table. After breakfast, there were $1\frac{2}{3}$ cakes left. How many cakes were eaten?

7. A container has a capacity of 3 litres. It contains $1\frac{3}{4}$ litres of water. How much more water is needed to fill the container?

8. Ann planned to spend $1\frac{1}{2}$ hours to cook a meal. She finished the cooking in $1\frac{1}{12}$ hours. How much earlier did she finish the cooking?

9. The total length of two ribbon is $2\frac{3}{4}$ m. If one ribbon is $1\frac{1}{3}$ m long, what is the length of the other ribbon?

4 Product of a Fraction and a Whole Number

Lihua bought 12 eggs. She used $\frac{2}{3}$ of them to bake a cake. How many eggs did she use?

Method 1:

Divide 12 eggs into 3 equal groups.

2 groups are shaded to show $\frac{2}{3}$.

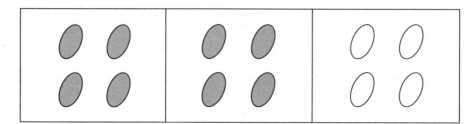

$\frac{2}{3}$ of 12 = ■

She used ■ eggs.

Method 2:

Write $\frac{2}{3}$ of 12 as $\frac{2}{3} \times 12$.

$$\frac{2}{3} \times 12 = \frac{2 \times 12}{3}$$

$$= ■$$

She used ■ eggs.

1. (a) Multiply $\frac{2}{3}$ by 5.

$$\frac{2}{3} \times 5 = \frac{2 \times 5}{3}$$

$$= \blacksquare$$

$$\frac{2}{3} \times 5 = 5 \times \frac{2}{3}$$

(b) Multiply 5 by $\frac{2}{3}$.

$$5 \times \frac{2}{3} = \frac{5 \times 2}{3}$$

$$= \blacksquare$$

2. Find the value of $\frac{3}{8} \times 20$.

Method 1:

$$\frac{3}{8} \times 20 = \frac{3 \times 20}{8}$$

$$= \frac{60}{8}$$

$$= \blacksquare$$

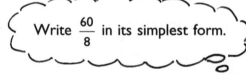

Write $\frac{60}{8}$ in its simplest form.

Method 2:

$$\frac{3}{8} \times 20 = \frac{3 \times \overset{5}{\cancel{20}}}{\underset{2}{\cancel{8}}}$$

$$= \frac{3 \times 5}{2}$$

$$= \blacksquare$$

4 is a common factor of 20 and 8.
Divide 20 and 8 by 4.

Method 3:

$$\frac{3}{\underset{2}{\cancel{8}}} \times \overset{5}{\cancel{20}} = \frac{3 \times 5}{2}$$

$$= \blacksquare$$

3. How many months are there in $\frac{5}{6}$ of a year?

$$\frac{5}{6} \text{ of a year} = \frac{5}{6} \times 12 \text{ months}$$

$$= \blacksquare \text{ months}$$

1 year = 12 months

Conversion of Measurements

Length
1 m = 100 cm
1 km = 1000 m

Weight
1 kg = 1000 g

Volume of liquid/capacity
1 ℓ = 1000 ml

Time
1 year = 12 months
1 week = 7 days
1 day = 24 hours
1 hour = 60 minutes
1 minute = 60 seconds

4. Find the missing number in each $\blacksquare$.

(a) $\frac{1}{2}$ min = $\blacksquare$ s

(b) $\frac{7}{10}$ kg = $\blacksquare$ g

(c) $\frac{2}{5}$ km = $\blacksquare$ m

(d) $\frac{3}{10}$ ℓ = $\blacksquare$ ml

(e) $\frac{3}{4}$ year = $\blacksquare$ months

(f) $\frac{1}{6}$ h = $\blacksquare$ min

5. Express $2\frac{3}{4}$ h in hours and minutes.

$$\frac{3}{4} \text{ h} = \frac{3}{4} \times 60 \text{ min} = \blacksquare \text{ min}$$

$$2\frac{3}{4} \text{ h} = \blacksquare \text{ h } \blacksquare \text{ min}$$

6. Find the missing number in each $\blacksquare$.

(a) $2\frac{1}{3}$ h = $\blacksquare$ h $\blacksquare$ min

(b) $4\frac{2}{3}$ min = $\blacksquare$ min $\blacksquare$ s

(c) $5\frac{1}{4}$ m = $\blacksquare$ m $\blacksquare$ cm

(d) $3\frac{1}{2}$ km = $\blacksquare$ km $\blacksquare$ m

(e) $14\frac{9}{10}$ ℓ = $\blacksquare$ ℓ $\blacksquare$ ml

(f) $6\frac{1}{4}$ years = $\blacksquare$ years $\blacksquare$ months

Workbook Exercise 19

7. Express $3\frac{2}{5}$ km in metres.

$$3 \text{ km} = 3000 \text{ m}$$

$$\frac{2}{5} \text{ km} = \frac{2}{5} \times 1000 \text{ m}$$

$$= \blacksquare \text{ m}$$

$$3\frac{2}{5} \text{ km} = \blacksquare \text{ m}$$

$3\frac{2}{5}$ km = 3 km + $\frac{2}{5}$ km

8. Express $2\frac{1}{4}$ days in hours.

$$2 \text{ days} = \blacksquare \text{ h}$$

$$\frac{1}{4} \text{ day} = \blacksquare \text{ h}$$

$$2\frac{1}{4} \text{ days} = \blacksquare \text{ h}$$

9. Find the missing number in each $\blacksquare$.

(a) $2\frac{1}{2}$ m = $\blacksquare$ cm   (b) $1\frac{9}{10}$ kg = $\blacksquare$ g (c) $3\frac{1}{2}$ days = $\blacksquare$ h

(d) $2\frac{3}{4}$ years = $\blacksquare$ months (e) $1\frac{3}{10}$ ℓ = $\blacksquare$ ml (f) $4\frac{1}{3}$ min = $\blacksquare$ s

(g) $2\frac{1}{10}$ km = $\blacksquare$ m   (h) $3\frac{1}{3}$ h = $\blacksquare$ min (i) $5\frac{3}{4}$ m = $\blacksquare$ cm

> Workbook Exercise 20

10. (a) What fraction of \$2 is 80¢?

$$\$2 = 200¢$$

$$\frac{80}{200} = \blacksquare$$

\$1 = 100¢

(b) Express 600 ml as a fraction of 1 litre.
(c) Express 90 cm as a fraction of 3 m.
(d) Express 45 seconds as a fraction of 1 minute.
(e) Express 50 minutes as a fraction of 2 hours.

> Workbook Exercise 21

PRACTICE 3D

Find the value of each of the following in its simplest form.

	(a)	(b)	(c)
1.	$\frac{1}{2} \times 14$	$\frac{1}{4} \times 26$	$\frac{2}{5} \times 40$
2.	$30 \times \frac{4}{5}$	$40 \times \frac{2}{3}$	$15 \times \frac{5}{9}$
3.	$\frac{7}{3} \times 21$	$\frac{13}{5} \times 20$	$40 \times \frac{9}{8}$

Find the missing number in each ■.

	(a)	(b)
4.	$\frac{2}{3}$ h = ■ min	$\frac{3}{5}$ kg = ■ g
5.	$\frac{4}{5}$ m = ■ cm	$\frac{9}{10}$ km = ■ m
6.	$8\frac{3}{4}$ years = ■ years ■ months	$3\frac{3}{5}$ ℓ = ■ ℓ ■ ml
7.	$9\frac{1}{4}$ kg = ■ kg ■ g	$5\frac{1}{3}$ h = ■ h ■ min
8.	$3\frac{1}{2}$ m = ■ cm	$4\frac{1}{4}$ h = ■ min
9.	$2\frac{7}{10}$ km = ■ m	$4\frac{2}{3}$ days = ■ h

10. (a) What fraction of $1 is 90¢?
     (b) What fraction of 2 ℓ is 750 ml?

11. (a) Express 9 months as a fraction of 1 year.
     (b) Express 50 minutes as a fraction of 2 hours.

12. In an examination, 40 out of 44 pupils passed. What fraction of the pupils passed the examination?

13. Minah earns $350 a month. She saves $70 each month. What fraction of her earnings does she save?

⑤ Product of Fractions

(a) Colour $\frac{3}{4}$ of a rectangle.

Cut out $\frac{1}{2}$ of the coloured parts.

What fraction of the rectangle is cut out?

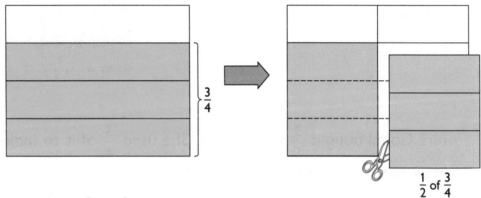

$$\frac{1}{2} \text{ of } \frac{3}{4} = \frac{3}{8}$$

$\frac{3}{8}$ of the rectangle is cut out.

$$\frac{1}{2} \times \frac{3}{4} = \frac{1 \times 3}{2 \times 4}$$

$$= \frac{3}{8}$$

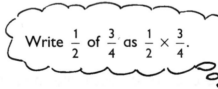

Write $\frac{1}{2}$ of $\frac{3}{4}$ as $\frac{1}{2} \times \frac{3}{4}$.

(b) Colour $\frac{1}{2}$ of a rectangle.

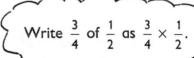

Write $\frac{3}{4}$ of $\frac{1}{2}$ as $\frac{3}{4} \times \frac{1}{2}$.

Cut out $\frac{3}{4}$ of the coloured parts.

What fraction of the rectangle is cut out?

Is $\frac{1}{2}$ of $\frac{3}{4}$ the same as $\frac{3}{4}$ of $\frac{1}{2}$?

1. A flower garden occupies $\frac{1}{2}$ of a piece of land. $\frac{3}{5}$ of the garden is used for growing orchids. What fraction of the land is used for growing orchids?

   $\frac{3}{5} \times \frac{1}{2} = $ ■

   ■ of the land is used for growing orchids.

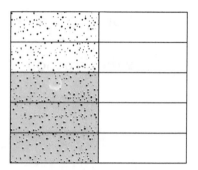

2. Mrs Gopal bought $\frac{3}{5}$ kg of sugar. She used $\frac{3}{4}$ of it to make a cake. How much sugar did she use?

   $\frac{3}{4} \times \frac{3}{5} = $ ■

   She used ■ kg of sugar.

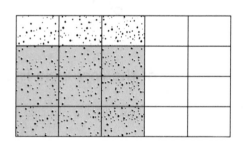

3. Find the area of a rectangle measuring $\frac{1}{3}$ m by $\frac{5}{6}$ m.

   $\frac{1}{3} \times \frac{5}{6} = $ ■

   The area of the rectangle is ■ m².

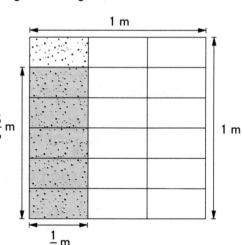

4. $\frac{2}{3}$ of a wall is painted red. $\frac{1}{4}$ of the remaining part is painted grey. What fraction of the wall is painted grey?

$$1 - \frac{2}{3} = \frac{1}{3}$$

The remaining part is $\frac{1}{3}$ of the wall.

$$\frac{1}{4} \times \frac{1}{3} = \blacksquare$$

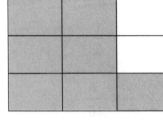

$\blacksquare$ of the wall is painted grey.

5. Multiply $\frac{4}{5}$ by $\frac{2}{3}$.

$$\frac{4}{5} \times \frac{2}{3} = \frac{4 \times 2}{5 \times 3}$$
$$= \blacksquare$$

6. Find the product of $\frac{9}{10}$ and $\frac{5}{12}$.

Method 1:

$$\frac{9}{10} \times \frac{5}{12} = \frac{^3\cancel{9} \times \cancel{5}^{\,1}}{_2\cancel{10} \times \cancel{12}_4}$$
$$= \blacksquare$$

Method 2:

$$\frac{^3\cancel{9}}{_2\cancel{10}} \times \frac{\cancel{5}^{\,1}}{\cancel{12}_4} = \frac{3 \times 1}{2 \times 4}$$
$$= \blacksquare$$

7. Find the value of

(a) $\frac{1}{2}$ of $\frac{1}{2}$

(b) $\frac{1}{3}$ of $\frac{3}{4}$

(c) $\frac{1}{4}$ of $\frac{8}{9}$

(d) $\frac{5}{6} \times \frac{1}{5}$

(e) $\frac{3}{4} \times \frac{5}{6}$

(f) $\frac{4}{5} \times \frac{3}{8}$

(g) $\frac{5}{8} \times \frac{4}{9}$

(h) $\frac{1}{3} \times \frac{6}{7}$

(i) $\frac{5}{6} \times \frac{7}{10}$

(j) $\frac{15}{4} \times \frac{8}{3}$

(k) $\frac{9}{4} \times \frac{16}{3}$

(l) $\frac{12}{5} \times \frac{20}{9}$

Workbook Exercises 22 & 23

PRACTICE 3E

Find the value of each of the following in its simplest form.

	(a)	(b)	(c)
1.	$\dfrac{3}{8} \times \dfrac{1}{3}$	$\dfrac{4}{9} \times \dfrac{5}{8}$	$\dfrac{7}{8} \times \dfrac{3}{7}$
2.	$\dfrac{2}{7} \times \dfrac{7}{10}$	$\dfrac{8}{9} \times \dfrac{3}{4}$	$\dfrac{9}{10} \times \dfrac{5}{6}$
3.	$\dfrac{5}{6} \times \dfrac{2}{5}$	$\dfrac{3}{4} \times \dfrac{2}{3}$	$\dfrac{3}{10} \times \dfrac{5}{6}$
4.	$\dfrac{16}{3} \times \dfrac{9}{4}$	$\dfrac{14}{9} \times \dfrac{12}{7}$	$\dfrac{10}{7} \times \dfrac{14}{5}$
5.	$\dfrac{20}{7} \times \dfrac{7}{4}$	$\dfrac{11}{5} \times \dfrac{20}{11}$	$\dfrac{15}{8} \times \dfrac{8}{3}$

6. Sumin had a piece of string $\dfrac{1}{2}$ m long. He used $\dfrac{1}{3}$ of it to tie a box. Find the length of the string which was used to tie the box.

7. Mrs Wu had $\dfrac{3}{4}$ litre of cooking oil. She used $\dfrac{2}{5}$ of it to fry prawn crackers. How much oil did she use?

8. Mrs Chen bought $\dfrac{4}{5}$ kg of beef. She cooked $\dfrac{3}{4}$ of it for lunch. How much beef did she cook?

9. Sally ate $\dfrac{1}{6}$ of a cake and gave $\dfrac{1}{5}$ of the remainder to her sister. What fraction of the cake did she give away?

10. Find the area of a rectangle which measures $\dfrac{5}{8}$ m by $\dfrac{3}{5}$ m.

6 Dividing a Fraction by a Whole Number

4 boys shared $\frac{2}{3}$ of a pie equally.

What fraction of the pie did each boy receive?

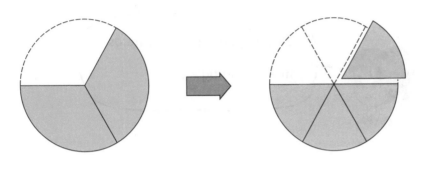

$$\frac{2}{3} \div 4 = \frac{1}{6}$$

Each boy received $\frac{1}{6}$ of the pie.

$$\frac{2}{3} \div 4 = \frac{1}{4} \text{ of } \frac{2}{3}$$

$$= \frac{1}{{}_2 4} \times \frac{\cancel{2}^{\,1}}{3}$$

$$= \frac{1}{6}$$

Each boy received $\frac{1}{4}$ of $\frac{2}{3}$ of the pie.

Here is another way to divide $\frac{2}{3}$ by 4.

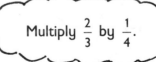

Multiply $\frac{2}{3}$ by $\frac{1}{4}$.

$$\frac{2}{3} \div 4 = \frac{\cancel{2}^{\,1}}{3} \times \frac{1}{\cancel{4}_2}$$

$$= \frac{1}{6}$$

1. Divide $\frac{2}{3}$ by 3.

$$\frac{2}{3} \div 3 = \frac{2}{3} \times \frac{1}{3}$$

$$= \blacksquare$$

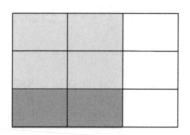

Dividing by 3 is the same as multiplying by $\frac{1}{3}$.

2. Divide.

(a) $\frac{3}{4} \div 6 = \frac{3}{4} \times \frac{1}{6}$

$= \blacksquare$

(b) $\frac{3}{5} \div 9 = \frac{3}{5} \times \frac{1}{9}$

$= \blacksquare$

(c) $\frac{5}{6} \div 5 = \frac{5}{6} \times \blacksquare$

$= \blacksquare$

(d) $\frac{9}{10} \div 3 = \frac{9}{10} \times \blacksquare$

$= \blacksquare$

3. Find the value of each of the following in its simplest form.

(a) $\frac{1}{3} \div 2$

(b) $\frac{4}{5} \div 3$

(c) $\frac{5}{7} \div 4$

(d) $\frac{4}{5} \div 4$

(e) $\frac{6}{7} \div 2$

(f) $\frac{2}{3} \div 8$

(g) $\frac{9}{16} \div 3$

(h) $\frac{3}{8} \div 6$

(i) $\frac{9}{10} \div 6$

Workbook Exercises 24 & 25

PRACTICE 3F

Find the value of each of the following in its simplest form.

	(a)	(b)	(c)
1.	$\frac{1}{3} \div 3$	$\frac{5}{6} \div 3$	$\frac{9}{10} \div 3$
2.	$\frac{3}{4} \div 5$	$\frac{1}{5} \div 4$	$\frac{8}{9} \div 6$
3.	$\frac{2}{5} \div 3$	$\frac{5}{9} \div 5$	$\frac{5}{6} \div 10$

4. A string of length $\frac{4}{5}$ m is cut into 2 equal pieces. What is the length of each piece?

5. $\frac{4}{5}$ of the money collected at a jumble sale was divided equally among 4 clubs. What fraction of the money did each club receive?

6. 6 packets of biscuits weigh $\frac{3}{10}$ kg. Find the weight of 1 packet of biscuits.

7. Siti poured $\frac{2}{5}$ litre of fruit juice equally into 4 cups. How much fruit juice was there in each cup?

8. The perimeter of a square flower bed is $\frac{3}{4}$ m. Find the length of each side in metres.

9. Mrs Gomez divided $\frac{3}{4}$ kg of grapes equally among 6 children. How many kilograms of grapes did each child receive?

7 Word Problems

Meili had $125. She spent $\frac{2}{5}$ of the money and saved the rest.
How much money did she save?

$$1 - \frac{2}{5} = \frac{3}{5}$$

She saved $\frac{3}{5}$ of the money.

First, I find what fraction of the money is saved.

$$\frac{3}{5} \times \$125 = \$\blacksquare$$

She saved $\blacksquare.

I do it in another way.

Amount of money spent $= \dfrac{2}{{}_1\cancel{5}} \times \$\cancel{125}^{25} = \$50$

Amount of money saved $= \$125 - \$50 = \$\blacksquare$

Here is yet another way.
I find 1 unit first.

$ 125

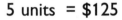

5 units $= \$125$

1 unit $= \$\blacksquare$

Amount of money saved $= 3$ units $= \$\blacksquare$

56

1. There are **96** children in a library. $\frac{5}{8}$ of them are girls. How many boys are there?

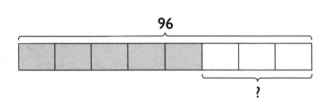

8 units = 96

3 units = ?

2. David had **$40**. He spent $\frac{1}{5}$ of the money on a storybook and $\frac{3}{10}$ on a calculator. How much did he spend altogether?

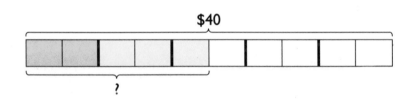

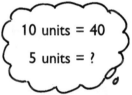

10 units = 40

5 units = ?

3. Mr Fu had some eggs. He sold $\frac{5}{8}$ of them. If he sold **300** eggs, how many eggs had he at first?

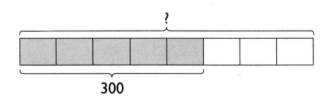

Workbook Exercises 26 & 27

4. Jim had 360 stamps. He sold $\frac{1}{3}$ of them on Monday and $\frac{1}{4}$ of the remainder on Tuesday. How many stamps did he sell on Tuesday?

Method 1:

$$1 - \frac{1}{3} = \frac{2}{3}$$

First, I find what fraction of the stamps were left on Monday.

He had $\frac{2}{3}$ of the stamps left on Monday.

$$\frac{2}{\cancel{3}_1} \times \cancel{360}^{120} = 2 \times 120 = 240$$

Next, I find the number of stamps left on Monday.

He had 240 stamps left on Monday.

$$\frac{1}{4} \times 240 = \blacksquare$$

He sold ◼ stamps on Tuesday.

Method 2:

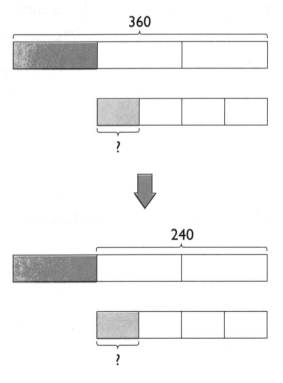

360

?

240

?

3 parts = 360
1 part = 120
2 parts = 240

Number of stamps left on Monday = 4 units = 240

Number of stamps sold on Tuesday = 1 unit = ◼

5. Mrs Lin made 300 tarts. She sold $\frac{3}{4}$ of them and gave $\frac{1}{3}$ of the remainder to her neighbour. How many tarts had she left?

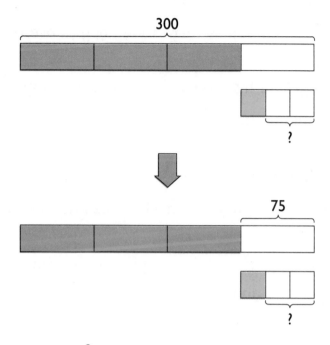

6. Encik Hassan gave $\frac{2}{5}$ of his money to his wife and spent $\frac{1}{2}$ of the remainder. If he had $300 left, how much money did he have at first?

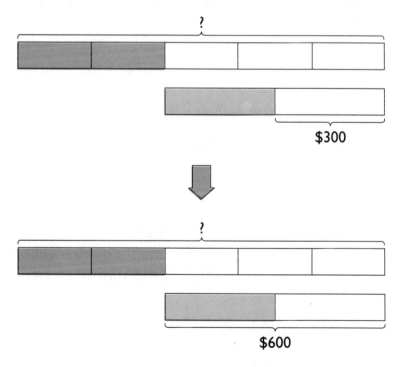

Workbook Exercises 28 & 29

PRACTICE 3G

1. $\frac{3}{7}$ of the apples in a box are red apples. The rest are green apples. There are 24 green apples. How many apples are there altogether?

2. After spending $\frac{2}{5}$ of his money on a toy car, Samy had $42 left. How much money did he have at first?

3. Mr Wang had $400. He spent $\frac{2}{5}$ of it on a vacuum cleaner and $\frac{1}{4}$ of the remainder on a fan. How much money had he left?

4. A hawker sold $\frac{2}{3}$ of his curry puffs in the morning and $\frac{1}{6}$ in the afternoon. He sold 200 curry puffs altogether. How many curry puffs had he left?

5. Mrs Chen bought some eggs. She used $\frac{1}{2}$ of them to make tarts and $\frac{1}{4}$ of the remainder to make a cake. She had 9 eggs left. How many eggs did she buy?

6. Minghua bought a bag of marbles. $\frac{1}{4}$ of the marbles were blue, $\frac{1}{8}$ were green and $\frac{1}{5}$ of the remainder were yellow. If there were 24 yellow marbles, how many marbles did he buy?

7. Mr Li gave $\frac{1}{4}$ of a sum of money to his wife. Then he divided the remainder equally among his 4 children.
   (a) What fraction of the sum of money did each child receive?
   (b) If each child received $600, find the sum of money.

8. Rosni read 10 pages of a book on Monday. She read $\frac{1}{3}$ of the remainder on Tuesday. If she still had 24 pages to read, how many pages were there in the book?

REVIEW A

1. Write the following in figures.
   (a) Five hundred and fifteen thousand, four hundred and seven
   (b) Four million and six hundred thousand

2. Write the following in words.
   (a) 872 520   (b) 1 034 000   (c) 4 500 000   (d) 162 003

3. What is the value of the digit 9 in 9 364 000?

4. Which one of the following numbers has the digit 6 in the ten thousands place?
   6 541 000, 640 059, 546 109, 5 164 000

5. (a) Round off $437 549 to the nearest $1000.
   (b) Round off 42 652 km to the nearest 1000 km.

6. The population of Marina Town is 280 524. Round off the number to the nearest 1000.

7. A bungalow is sold for about $2 400 000. Which one of the following could be the actual selling price of the bungalow?
   $2 356 000, $2 299 000, $2 460 000, $2 310 000

8. (a) Write down a common factor of 24 and 32.
   (b) Write down a common multiple of 8 and 10.

9. Round each number to the nearest 1000.
   Then estimate the value of
   (a) 3472 + 1607   (b) 29 074 + 5872
   (c) 9035 − 5712   (d) 14 236 − 6223

10. What is the missing number in each ■?
    3600, ■, 4800, 5400, ■

11. Estimate the value of
    (a) 3268 × 7   (b) 4825 × 63
    (c) 4312 ÷ 6   (d) 7134 ÷ 82

12. Multiply or divide.
    (a) 2650 × 600   (b) 1245 × 4000   (c) 34 400 × 80
    (d) 1280 ÷ 80   (e) 1290 ÷ 80   (f) 84 000 ÷ 7000

13. Multiply or divide.
    (a) 36×28 (b) 52×75 (c) 615×32
    (d) $994 \div 71$ (e) $864 \div 36$ (f) $301 \div 24$

14. Find the value of each of the following:
    (a) $2 \times (28 + 36) - 49$ (b) $78 + 21 \div 3 - (6 + 25)$
    (c) $50 - (225 \div 15 + 13)$ (d) $29 + (300 \div 10 - 3 \times 9)$
    (e) $28 + 19 - 24$ (f) $12 - 9 \times 5 \div 15$
    (g) $(42 + 14) \div 7 \times 5$ (h) $(59 + 13) \div (4 \times 2)$

15. Write each fraction in its simplest form.
    (a) $\dfrac{6}{8}$ (b) $\dfrac{9}{15}$ (c) $\dfrac{16}{24}$ (d) $\dfrac{32}{40}$

16. Express each of the following as an improper fraction.
    (a) $5\dfrac{3}{8}$ (b) $3\dfrac{7}{11}$ (c) $4\dfrac{5}{9}$ (d) $2\dfrac{3}{4}$

17. Express each of the following as a whole number or a mixed number in its simplest form.
    (a) $\dfrac{20}{6}$ (b) $\dfrac{18}{4}$ (c) $\dfrac{33}{3}$ (d) $\dfrac{30}{8}$

18. Name two equivalent fractions for each of these fractions.
    (a) $\dfrac{3}{4}$ (b) $\dfrac{2}{6}$ (c) $\dfrac{5}{9}$ (d) $\dfrac{11}{14}$

19. Divide. Express each answer as a fraction in its simplest form.
    (a) $8 \div 12$ (b) $15 \div 54$ (c) $63 \div 18$ (d) $100 \div 35$

20. Which is greater?
    (a) $\dfrac{3}{2}$ or $\dfrac{5}{4}$ (b) $2\dfrac{1}{2}$ or $2\dfrac{1}{7}$ (c) $3\dfrac{8}{9}$ or 4

    (d) $1\dfrac{6}{7}$ or $\dfrac{12}{7}$ (e) $4\dfrac{2}{3}$ or $\dfrac{9}{2}$ (f) $3\dfrac{1}{6}$ or $\dfrac{16}{5}$

21. Arrange the fractions in order, beginning with the smallest.
    (a) $1\dfrac{3}{4}$, $\dfrac{9}{4}$, $1\dfrac{5}{8}$, $\dfrac{9}{2}$ (b) $1\dfrac{2}{8}$, $\dfrac{36}{5}$, $1\dfrac{2}{3}$, $\dfrac{8}{2}$

22. What number must be added to $4\dfrac{2}{9}$ to make 5?

62

23. How many quarters are there in $3\frac{1}{4}$?

24. Add or subtract. Give each answer in its simplest form.

    (a) $\frac{5}{6} + \frac{3}{4}$

    (b) $3\frac{3}{8} + \frac{5}{12}$

    (c) $2\frac{1}{2} + 5\frac{4}{5}$

    (d) $6 - \frac{6}{7}$

    (e) $4\frac{3}{4} - \frac{2}{3}$

    (f) $6\frac{1}{3} - 2\frac{3}{5}$

25. Multiply or divide.

    (a) $\frac{7}{20} \times 4$

    (b) $24 \times \frac{5}{8}$

    (c) $35 \times \frac{2}{5}$

    (d) $\frac{3}{4} \times \frac{8}{9}$

    (e) $\frac{5}{8} \times \frac{14}{15}$

    (f) $\frac{8}{12} \times \frac{16}{20}$

    (g) $\frac{3}{5} \div 3$

    (h) $\frac{7}{8} \div 2$

    (i) $\frac{4}{7} \div 12$

26. (a) Express $\frac{3}{5}$ m in centimetres.

    (b) Express $1\frac{7}{10}$ kg in kilograms and grams.

27. (a) Express 4 months as a fraction of 1 year.

    (b) Express 48 minutes as a fraction of $1\frac{1}{2}$ hours.

28. Mrs Wu had 600 cookies. She packed them into packets of 24. How many packets of cookies did she get?

29. There are 2204 children in a school. 925 of them are girls. How many more boys than girls are there?

30. 3 pieces of ribbon, each 85 cm long, are cut from a length of ribbon 3 m long. What is the length of the remaining piece of ribbon?

31. Peter, John and Dan shared $1458 equally. Peter used part of his share to buy a bicycle and had $139 left. What was the cost of the bicycle?

32. Oranges are packed in a box in 4 layers. Each layer has 6 rows of oranges with 8 oranges in each row. How many oranges are there in the box?

33. Mrs Chen has 1400 tarts. If she sells all of them at 80 cents each, how much money will she receive?

34. Rosni answered 28 out of 32 sums correctly. What fraction of the sums did she answer correctly?

35. Mrs Wu bought $2\frac{1}{5}$ kg of potatoes and $1\frac{1}{2}$ kg of carrots. How much more potatoes than carrots did she buy?

36. There are 42 pupils in Miss Li's class. $\frac{3}{7}$ of them wear spectacles. How many pupils wear spectacles?

37. Danny bought 6 packets of drink. Each packet contained $\frac{1}{4}$ litre of drink. Find the total amount of drink in litres.

38. Cik Aminah had $\frac{3}{5}$ kg of sugar. She used $\frac{1}{4}$ of it to make biscuits. How much sugar did she use to make the biscuits?

39. Mrs Chen bought $\frac{1}{2}$ of a cake. She cut it into 4 equal pieces. What fraction of the whole cake is each piece?

40. Mr Hassan spent $\frac{1}{3}$ of his salary on food and $\frac{2}{5}$ of the remainder on transport.
    (a) What fraction of his salary had he left?
    (b) If he had $600 left, find his salary.

41. Mrs Li bought 6 m of cloth to make a skirt and 3 blouses. She used $1\frac{3}{4}$ m for the skirt and $\frac{3}{4}$ m for each blouse. How much cloth had she left?

42. Mr Li had 1280 eggs. He sold $\frac{3}{5}$ of them on Saturday and $\frac{1}{4}$ of the remainder on Sunday. Find the total number of eggs sold on the two days.

4 Area of Triangle

1 Finding the Area of a Triangle

Find the area of each shaded triangle and its related rectangle.

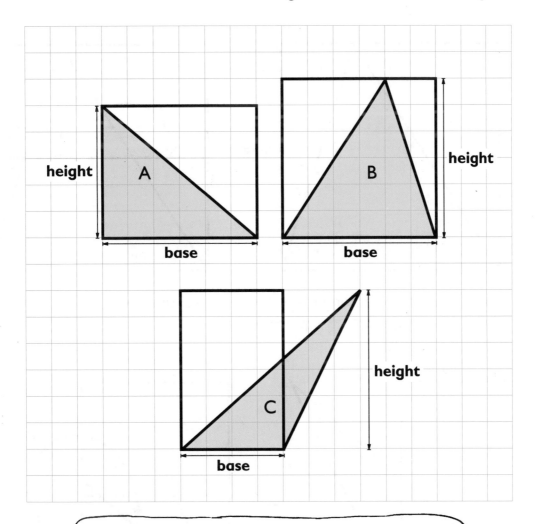

Compare the area of each triangle with the area of its related rectangle.

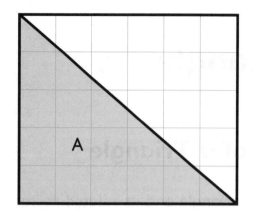

Area of related rectangle
= 6 × 5 = 30 square units

Area of triangle A
= ■ square units

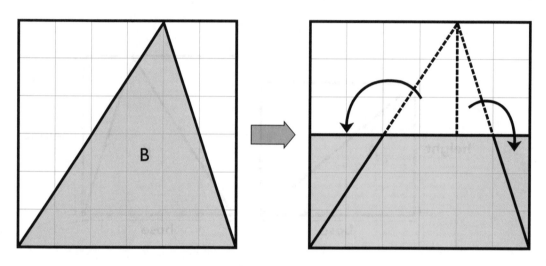

Area of related rectangle = 6 × 6 = 36 square units
Area of triangle B = ■ square units

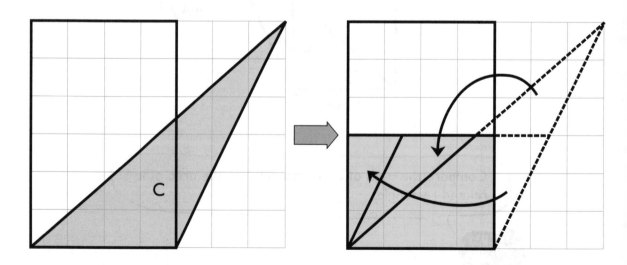

Area of related rectangle = 4 × 6 = 24 square units
Area of triangle C = ■ square units

Area of triangle = $\frac{1}{2}$ × Area of related rectangle

Area of triangle = $\frac{1}{2}$ × Base × Height

1. Find the area of each triangle.

(a)

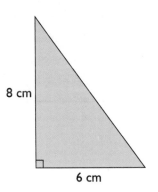

8 cm

6 cm

Area of the triangle

$= \frac{1}{2} \times 6 \times 8$

$= \blacksquare$ cm^2

(b)

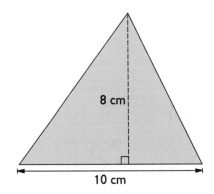

8 cm

10 cm

Area of the triangle

$= \frac{1}{2} \times 10 \times 8$

$= \blacksquare$ cm^2

(c)

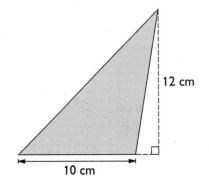

12 cm

10 cm

Area of the triangle

$= \frac{1}{2} \times 10 \times 12$

$= \blacksquare$ cm^2

2. Find the area of each shaded triangle.

(a)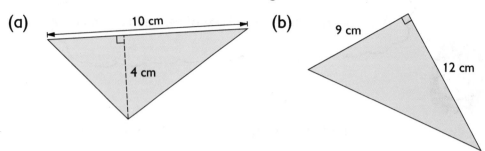

10 cm

4 cm

(b)

9 cm

12 cm

(c)

9 m

7 m

(d)

20 m

22 m

Workbook Exercises 30 to 32

3. Find the area of each shaded triangle.

(a)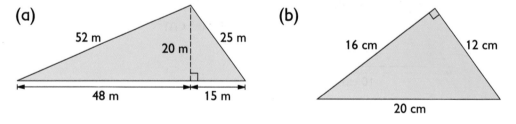

52 m   20 m   25 m

48 m   15 m

(b)

16 cm   12 cm

20 cm

(c)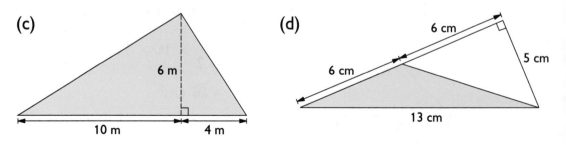

6 m

10 m   4 m

(d)

6 cm

6 cm

5 cm

13 cm

4. Find the shaded area of each rectangle.

(a)

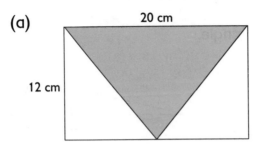

20 cm

12 cm

(b)

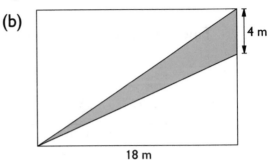

4 m

18 m

5. Find the shaded area of each rectangle.

(a)

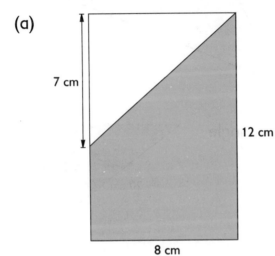

7 cm

12 cm

8 cm

In each figure, the unshaded part is a triangle.

Find the area of the triangle first.

(b)

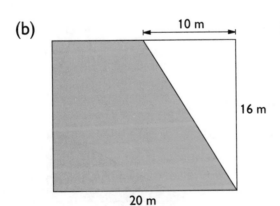

10 m

16 m

20 m

(c)

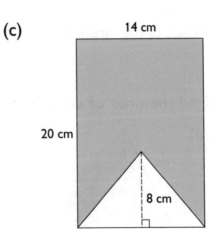

14 cm

20 cm

8 cm

Workbook Exercise 33

PRACTICE 4A

1. Find the area of each shaded triangle.

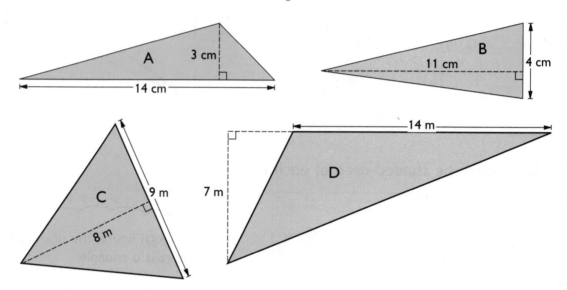

2. The perimeter of the shaded triangle is 60 cm. Find its area.

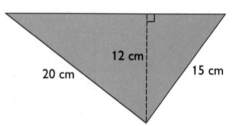

3. This figure is made up of 8 triangles. The base of each triangle is 6 cm and the height is 6 cm.
What is the area of the figure?

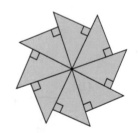

4. Find the area of each shaded figure.

(a)

(b)

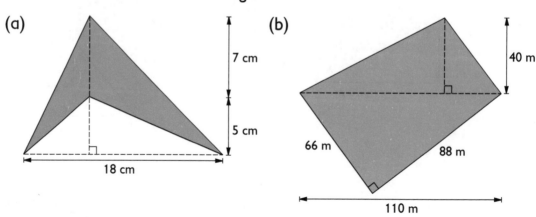

5 Ratio

1 Finding Ratio

David and John visited a stationery fair. David bought 3 bottles of blue ink and 2 bottles of red ink.

The **ratio** of the number of bottles of blue ink to the number of bottles of red ink is 3 : 2.

We read the ratio 3 : 2 as **3 to 2**.

John bought 5 boxes of blue pens and 2 boxes of red pens.

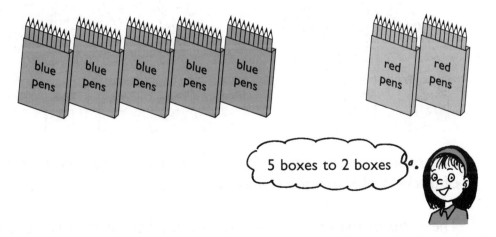

5 boxes to 2 boxes

The **ratio** of the number of blue pens to the number of red pens is 5 : 2.

1. Minghua mixed 3 tins of red paint with 1 tin of white paint.

The ratio of the amount of red paint to the amount of white paint is 3 : 1.

The ratio of the amount of white paint to the amount of red paint is ⬜ : ⬜.

2.

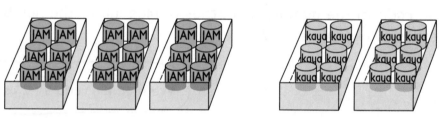

express by these units or batches as they did

The ratio of the number of cans of jam to the number of cans of kaya is 3 : 2.

The ratio of the number of cans of kaya to the number of cans of jam is ⬜ : ⬜.

3.

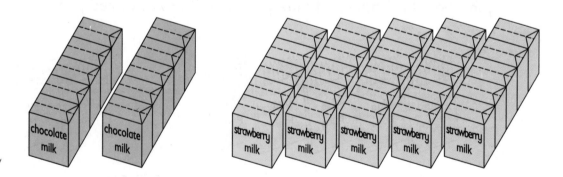

The ratio of the number of packets of chocolate milk to the number of packets of strawberry milk is ⬜ : ⬜.

The ratio of the number of packets of strawberry milk to the number of packets of chocolate milk is ⬜ : ⬜.

4.

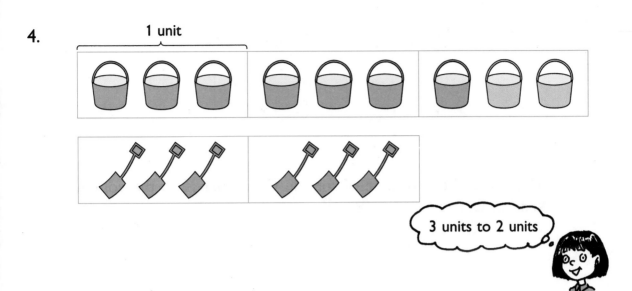

The ratio of the number of pails to the number of spades is 3 : 2 .

5.

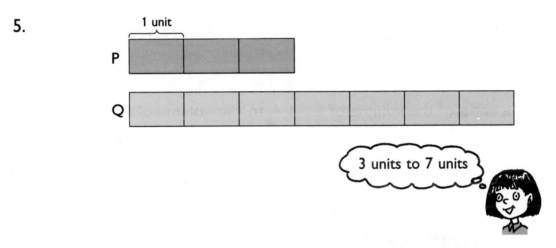

The ratio of the length of P to the length of Q is 3 : 7 .

6.

The ratio of the length of the rectangle to its breadth is 5 : 4 .

7.

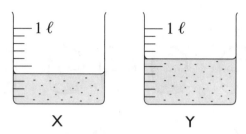

The ratio of the volume of sand in Container X to the volume of sand in Container Y is ☐ : ☐.

8.

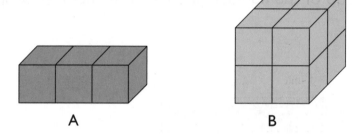

The ratio of the volume of Solid A to the volume of Solid B is ☐ : ☐.

9.

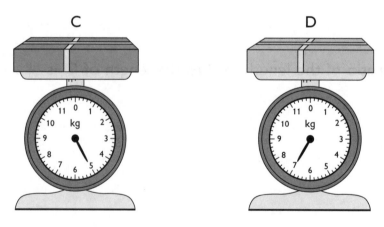

The ratio of the weight of Parcel C to the weight of Parcel D is ☐ : ☐.

Workbook Exercise 34

② Equivalent Ratios

John has $8 and Peter has $12.

The ratio of John's money to Peter's money is 8 : 12.

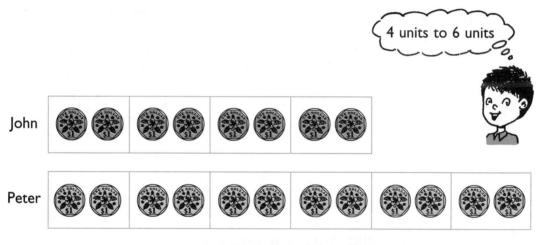

> 4 units to 6 units

The ratio of John's money to Peter's money is 4 : 6.

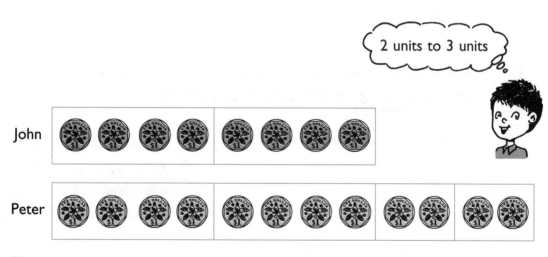

> 2 units to 3 units

The ratio of John's money to Peter's money is 2 : 3.

8 : 12, 4 : 6 and 2 : 3 are **equivalent ratios**.

2 : 3 is a ratio in its simplest form.

1. Write each ratio in its simplest form.
   (a) 4 : 10

   4 : 10 = 2 : 5

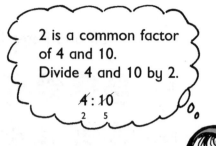

2 is a common factor
of 4 and 10.
Divide 4 and 10 by 2.

4 : 10
2   5

   (b) 12 : 18

   12 : 18 = 2 : 3

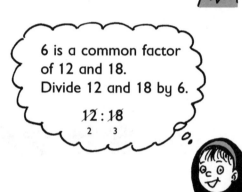

6 is a common factor
of 12 and 18.
Divide 12 and 18 by 6.

12 : 18
2   3

2. Write each ratio in its simplest form.
   (a) 8 : 10 4 : 5   (b) 10 : 6   5 : 3
   (c) 6 : 24 1 : 4   (d) 21 : 14 3 : 2

3. There are 15 ducks and 12 chickens in a farm. Find the ratio of the number of ducks to the number of chickens.

   15 : 12 = 5 : 4

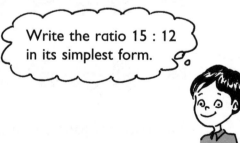

Write the ratio 15 : 12
in its simplest form.

The ratio of the number of ducks to the number of chickens is 4 : 5.

Workbook Exercise 35

4. There are 40 pupils in a class. 25 of them are boys.
Find the ratio of the number of boys to the number of girls in the class.

Number of girls = 40 − 25 = 15

Number of boys = 25

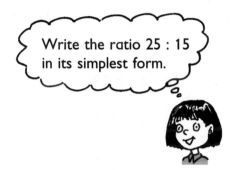

Write the ratio 25 : 15 in its simplest form.

25 : 15 = 5 : 3

The ratio of the number of boys to the number of girls is 5 : 3.

5. The ratio of the length of Ribbon A to the length of Ribbon B is 7 : 4.
If Ribbon A is 21 m long, find the length of Ribbon B.

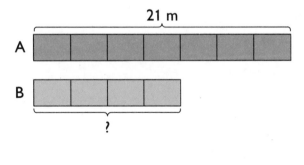

21 m

A

B

?

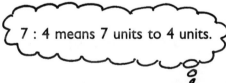

7 : 4 means 7 units to 4 units.

7 units = 21 m

1 unit = 3 m

4 units = 12 m

The length of Ribbon B is 12 m.

6. Siti and Mary shared $35 in the ratio 4 : 3.
How much money did Siti receive?

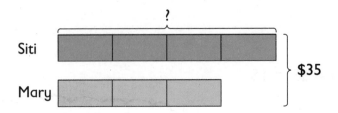

7 units = $35

1 unit = $5

4 units = $20

Siti received $20.

7. The ratio of the weight of Parcel X to the weight of Parcel Y is 5 : 3.
If the weight of Parcel X is 40 kg, find the total weight of the two
parcels.

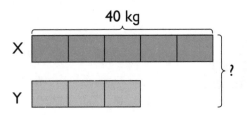

5 units = 40 kg

1 unit = 8 kg

8 units = 24 kg

The total weight is 64 kg.

Workbook Exercise 36

PRACTICE 5A

1.

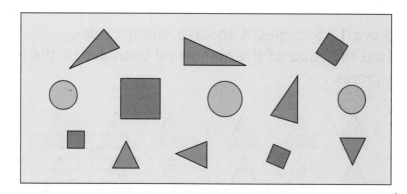

    (a) Find the ratio of the number of circles to the number of triangles. ☐ : ☐

    (b) Find the ratio of the number of triangles to the number of squares.   2 : 3   1st

2.   The length of a rectangle is 16 cm and its breadth is 12 cm. Find the ratio of the length of the rectangle to its breadth.

        4 : 3

3.   Ali won a cash prize of $50. He saved $35 and spent the rest. Find the ratio of the amount of money he saved to the amount of money he spent.   7 5

          how much did he spend ?
          write it in original terms +
          then simplify

4.   Mrs Tan made pineapple drinks by mixing pineapple syrup and water in the ratio 2 : 7. If she used 4 litres of pineapple syrup, how much water did she use?

        14 liters

5.   David cuts a rope 60 m long into two pieces in the ratio 2 : 3. What is the length of the shorter piece of rope?

        24 M

6.   The ratio of Samy's weight to John's weight is 6 : 5. If Samy weighs 48 kg, find John's weight.

        40 kg

7.   The ratio of the number of boys to the number of girls is 2 : 5. If there are 100 boys, how many children are there altogether?

        350

$$\frac{2}{5} = \frac{100}{x}$$

y = 250   + 100 = 350

3 Comparing Three Quantities

There are 12 triangles, 6 squares and 4 circles.

(a) Find the ratio of the number of triangles to the number of squares.

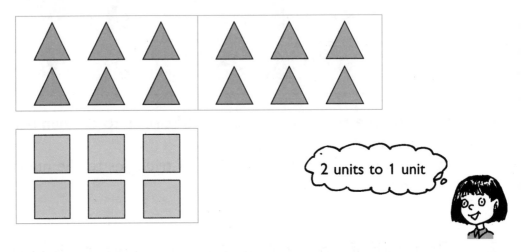

2 units to 1 unit

The ratio of the number of triangles to the number of squares is 2 : 1.

(b) Find the ratio of the number of triangles to the number of squares to the number of circles.

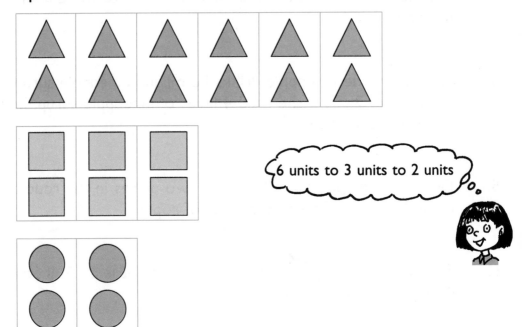

6 units to 3 units to 2 units

The ratio of the number of triangles to the number of squares to the number of circles is 6 : 3 : 2.

1. Write each ratio in its simplest form.
   (a) 12 : 6 : 4

   $$12 : 6 : 4 = 6 : 3 : 2$$

   2 is a common factor of
   12, 6 and 4.
   Divide 12, 6 and 4 by 2.

   12 : 6 : 4
   6   3   2

   (b) 20 : 10 : 15

   $$20 : 10 : 15 = 4 : 2 : 3$$

   5 is a common factor of
   20, 10 and 15.
   Divide 20, 10 and 15 by 5.

   20 : 10 : 15
   4   2   3

2. 20 litres of water are poured into 3 pails A, B and C in the ratio
   2 : 3 : 5.
   Find the volume of water in Pail C.

   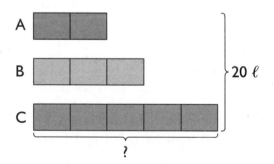

   10 units = 20 litres

   1 unit = 2 litres

   5 units = 10 litres

   The volume of water in Pail C is 10 litres.

   Workbook Exercises 37 & 38

PRACTICE 5B

1. In a school, there are 24 female teachers and 10 male teachers. What is the ratio of the number of male teachers to the number of female teachers?   5 : 12   w

2. In a fruit orchard, there are 60 mango trees, 20 durian trees and 35 rambutan trees.
   What is the ratio of the number of mango trees to the number of durian trees to the number of rambutan trees?   12 : 4 : 7

3. Mrs Wong cooked porridge by adding water to rice in the ratio 3 : 1. If she used 12 cups of water, how many cups of rice did she use?   4 cups

4. In a swimming club, the ratio of the number of boys to the number of girls is 7 : 4.
   If there are 121 children in the swimming club, how many boys are there?   77

5. William has $120. Ahmad has $20 less than William. What is the ratio of Ahmad's money to William's money?   6 : 5

6. A pole, 90 cm long, is painted green, white and black in the ratio 3 : 4 : 2.
   (a) What length of the pole is painted green? 30 cm
   (b) What length of the pole is painted black? 20 cm

7. Cement, sand and stone chippings are mixed in the ratio 1 : 2 : 4. The total volume of sand and stone chippings used is 24 m³.
   (a) Find the volume of cement in the mixture. 4 m³
   (b) Find the volume of sand in the mixture. 8 m³

8. The ratio of David's weight to Raju's weight to Ali's weight is 8 : 5 : 4. If Raju weighs 30 kg, find the total weight of the 3 boys.   102 kg

9. 3 boys share a sum of money in the ratio 5 : 3 : 2. If the smallest share is $30, find the biggest share. $75

6 Angles

1 Measuring Angles

What is the size of ∠m?

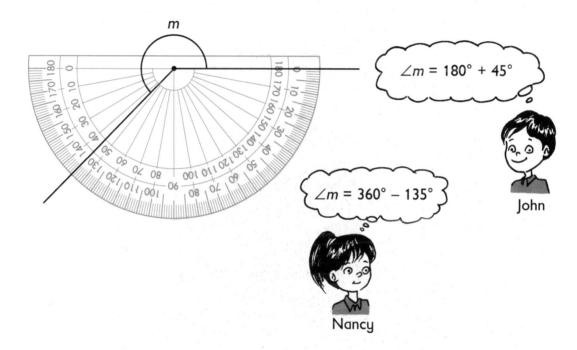

∠m = 180° + 45°

John

∠m = 360° − 135°

Nancy

Measure ∠n.

Which method shall I use?

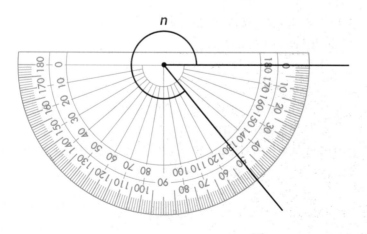

1. Estimate and then find each of the following marked angles by measurement.

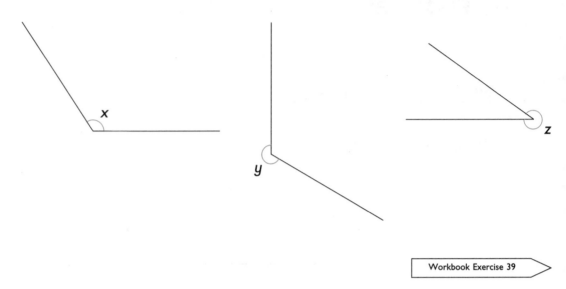

Workbook Exercise 39

2.

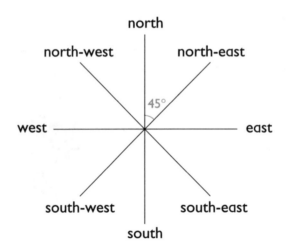

(a) You start facing north and turn clockwise to south-east.
     What angle do you turn through?
(b) You start facing west and turn anticlockwise to south-west.
     What angle do you turn through?

3. (a) You start facing north-west and turn clockwise through 90°.
         Which direction are you facing?
    (b) After turning anticlockwise through 225°, you end up facing east.
         Which direction were you facing at the start?

Workbook Exercise 40

② Finding Unknown Angles

When two straight lines cross, they form two pairs of **vertically opposite angles**.

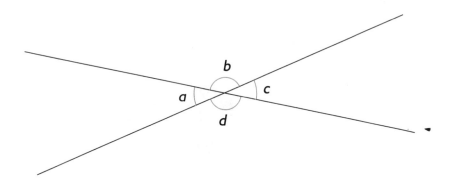

∠a and ∠c are vertically opposite angles.
∠b and ∠d are also vertically opposite angles.

∠a = 34°

∠b = ▮°

∠c = ▮°

∠d = ▮°

Vertically opposite angles are equal.

∠p, ∠q and ∠r are angles on a straight line.

∠p = 50°

∠q = ■°

∠r = ■°

∠p + ∠q + ∠r = ■°

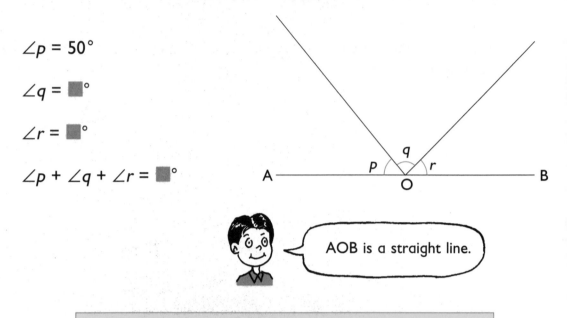

AOB is a straight line.

The sum of the angles on a straight line is 180°.

∠x, ∠y and ∠z are angles at a point.

∠x = 60°

∠y = ■°

∠z = ■°

∠x + ∠y + ∠z = ■°

The 3 marked angles meet at a common point.

The sum of the angles at a point is 360°.

1. Find the unknown marked angle in each of the following:

(a)

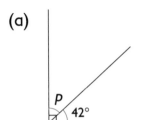

$\angle p = 90° - 42° = \blacksquare°$

(b)

$\angle q = 180° - 37° = \blacksquare°$

(c)

$\angle r = 360° - 15° = \blacksquare°$

2. The figure shows 4 angles formed by two straight lines.
If $\angle w = 46°$, find $\angle x$, $\angle y$ and $\angle z$.

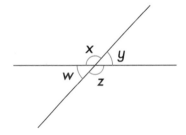

3. In the figure, AOB and COD are straight lines. Find $\angle$COB.

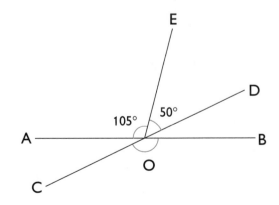

4. In the figure, ABC is a straight line.
∠ABD = 35° and ∠EBC = 55°. Find ∠DBE.

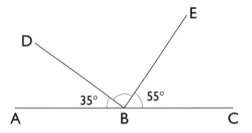

∠DBE = 180° − 35° − 55°

5. In the figure, find ∠x.

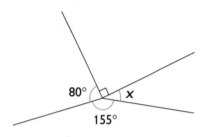

∠x = 360° − 90° − 80° − 155°

6. In the figure, find ∠m and ∠n.

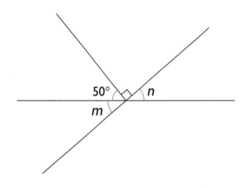

∠m and ∠n are vertically opposite angles.

7. Find the unknown marked angles.

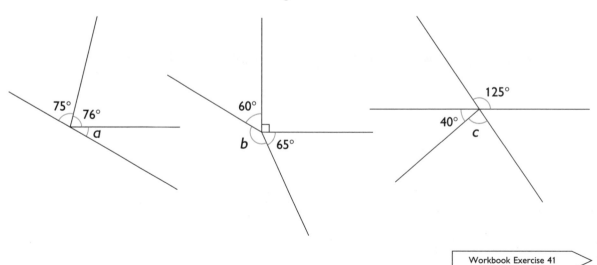

Workbook Exercise 41

88

REVIEW B

1. What number is 1000 less than 20 000?

2. Mr Li bought a car for $42 680.
   Round off this amount of money to the nearest $1000.

3. Find the value of each of the following:
   (a) 670×10 (b) 728×100 (c) 350×1000
   (d) $4300 \div 10$ (e) $58\,000 \div 100$ (f) $628\,000 \div 1000$

4. If ☆☆☆☆☆ represent 60, what number do ☆☆ represent?

5. What fraction of 3 litres is 800 ml?

6. Mr Chen had 24 durians. He sold 6 of them. What fraction of the durians did he sell?

7. An examination lasted $2\frac{1}{4}$ hours.
   Express $2\frac{1}{4}$ hours in hours and minutes.

8. A necklace is $\frac{3}{5}$ m long. Express $\frac{3}{5}$ m in centimetres.

9. Lily has $25. Mary has $10 more than Lily. Minah has 3 times as much money as Mary.
   (a) How much money does Minah have?
   (b) How much more money than Lily does Minah have?
   (c) How much money do the 3 girls have altogether?

10. Devi bought 8 m of string. She used $\frac{5}{8}$ of the string to make a flower-pot hanger. How much of the string had she left?

11. Mrs Lin cuts a raffia $\frac{4}{5}$ m long into 8 pieces of equal length. What is the length of each piece of raffia? Give the answer in metres.

12. Mr Chen had 64 durians. He sold $\frac{3}{4}$ of them. How many durians did he sell?

13. Mrs Chen had 2 kg of flour. She used $\frac{2}{5}$ of it to make buns. How much flour had she left? Give the answer in kilograms.

14. There are 1500 workers in a factory. $\frac{5}{6}$ of them are men. $\frac{3}{10}$ of the men are Malaysians. How many male Malaysian workers are there in the factory?

15. Mrs Li spent $\frac{3}{5}$ of her money on a refrigerator. The refrigerator cost $756. How much money had she left?

16. Ali saved twice as much as Ramat. Maria saved $60 more than Ramat. If they saved $600 altogether, how much did Maria save?

17. Ramat picked 257 rambutans from one tree and 493 from another. He sold all the rambutans at 50 for $3. How much money did he receive?

18. Mr Chen bought 40 boxes of oranges for $258. There were 24 oranges in each box. He threw away 15 rotten oranges and sold the rest at 3 for $1. How much money did he make?

19. John and Peter share $180 in the ratio 3 : 2. How much more money does John receive than Peter?

20. The ratio of the length of a rectangular field to its breadth is 4 : 3. The length of the field is 20 m. Find its area and perimeter.

21. Sumin, Raju and John shared a sum of money in the ratio 3 : 4 : 5. If Sumin received $30, what was the sum of money shared?

22. Find the area and the perimeter of the shaded figure.

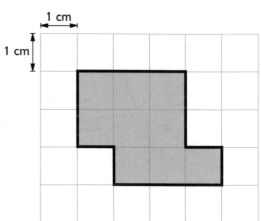

23. Find the perimeter and area of each figure. (All the angles are right angles.)

(a)

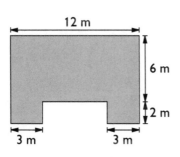

(b)

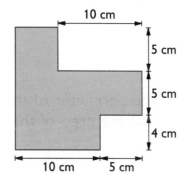

24. Estimate and then find the marked angles by measurement.

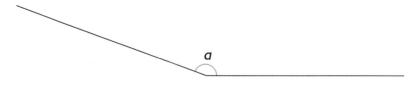

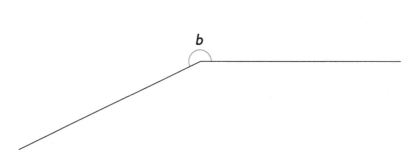

25. In each of the following figures, not drawn to scale, find ∠x.

(a)

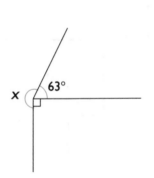

(b)

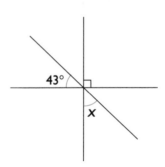

26. Find the area of each shaded triangle.

(a)

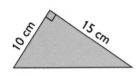

(b)

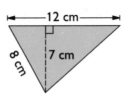

(c)

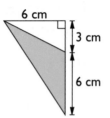

27. The perimeter of the triangle is 36 m.
Find the area of the triangle.

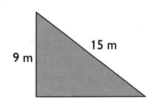

28. Find the shaded area of each rectangle.

(a)

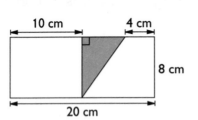

(b)

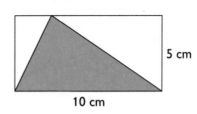

(c)

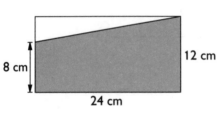

(d)

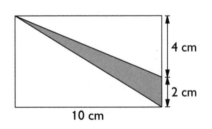

ANSWERS

Practice 1A

1. (a) 11 012 (b) 115 600
   (c) 700 013 (d) 880 005
   (e) 5 000 000 (f) 4 200 000
   (g) 10 000 000 (h) 808 000
2. (a) two hundred and seven thousand, three hundred and six
   (b) five hundred and sixty thousand and three
   (c) seven hundred thousand
   (d) three million, four hundred and fifty thousand
   (e) six million and twenty thousand
   (f) four million and three thousand
3. (a) 800 (b) 80 000
   (c) 80 (d) 800 000
   (e) 8000 (f) 8 000 000
4. (a) 6000 (b) 200 000
   (c) 184 900 (d) 7 609 000
   (e) 9 021 000 (f) 30 000
5. (a) 44 668, 45 668
   (b) 73 500, 74 500
   (c) 103 002, 113 002
   (d) 5 652 000, 5 662 000
   (e) 7 742 000, 5 742 000
6. (a) 53 607, 53 670, 53 760, 56 370
   (b) 324 468, 324 648, 342 468, 342 486
   (c) 425 700, 2 357 000, 2 537 000, 3 257 000

Practice 1B

1. (a) 70 (b) 660 (c) 1290
2. (a) 300 (b) 1300 (c) 20 800
3. (a) 7000 (b) 11 000 (c) 125 000
4. $800
5. $70 000
6. 1 000 000 km
7. (a) 180 000, 176 000, 171 000
   (b) 527 000
8. (a) 37 000 (b) 30 000
   (c) 38 000 (d) 48 000
   (e) 36 000 (f) 54 000
   (g) 900 (h) 600

Practice 1C

1. (a) 2380 (b) 70 000
   (c) 37 000 (d) 4000
   (e) 28 000 (f) 520 000

2. 392
   (a) 3920 (b) 39 200 (c) 392 000
3. 675
   (a) 6750 (b) 67 500 (c) 675 000
4. 9
   (a) 9000 (b) 900 (c) 90
5. 150
   (a) 1500 (b) 150 (c) 15
6. (a) 4 (b) 190 (c) 151
   (d) 51 (e) 700 (f) 103
7. (a) 56 (b) 300
   (c) 3 (d) 15
   (e) 37 (f) 68
   (g) 37 (h) 10
   (i) 21 (j) 70
   (k) 50 (l) 4
8. (a) 356 (b) 356
   (c) 298 (d) 298
   (e) 16 (f) 16
   (g) 64 (h) 63

Practice 1D

1. 71 kg
2. 48
3. 38
4. $15
5. 40
6. 170
7. $42
8. $10
9. $5
10. $35

Practice 2A

1. (a) 34 188 (b) 33 810 (c) 68 693
2. (a) 275 145 (b) 629 340 (c) 194 796
3. (a) 3 R17 (b) 2 R26 (c) 3 R2
4. (a) 53 (b) 6 R1 (c) 9 R28
5. (a) 19 (b) 38 R21 (c) 23 R33
6. (a) 98 R40 (b) 58 R6 (c) 179 R4
7. 432
8. 16 ℓ
9. 28
10. $56
11. $59 824
12. $35 064
13. 42
14. $105

93

Practice 3A

1. (a) $2\frac{3}{5}$ (b) 7

    (c) $2\frac{2}{3}$ (d) $8\frac{1}{3}$

2. (a) $3\frac{3}{4}$ (b) $5\frac{1}{4}$

    (c) $3\frac{1}{2}$ (d) $11\frac{1}{7}$

3. $3\frac{1}{4}$ m

4. $\frac{1}{3}$ m

5. $2\frac{1}{2}$

6. $\frac{2}{5}$ ℓ

7. $2\frac{1}{5}$ m

8. $\frac{2}{3}$ kg

Practice 3B

1. (a) $1\frac{5}{12}$ (b) $1\frac{1}{15}$ (c) $1\frac{17}{24}$

2. (a) $\frac{1}{4}$ (b) $\frac{2}{15}$ (d) $\frac{7}{12}$

3. (a) $\frac{7}{15}$ (b) $\frac{3}{4}$ (c) $\frac{13}{24}$

4. (a) $\frac{19}{24}$ (b) $\frac{19}{30}$ (c) $\frac{7}{15}$

5. $\frac{13}{20}$

6. $\frac{1}{2}$ h

7. (a) $\frac{3}{8}$ (b) $\frac{1}{8}$

8. (a) $\frac{17}{20}$ (b) $\frac{3}{20}$

Practice 3C

1. (a) $4\frac{2}{9}$ (b) $3\frac{23}{24}$ (c) $4\frac{1}{12}$

2. (a) $2\frac{1}{2}$ (b) $2\frac{1}{2}$ (c) $3\frac{7}{12}$

3. (a) $4\frac{7}{18}$ (b) $8\frac{1}{3}$ (c) $4\frac{5}{24}$

4. (a) $2\frac{1}{2}$ (b) $1\frac{1}{15}$ (c) $2\frac{2}{15}$

5. His brother, $1\frac{1}{10}$

6. $1\frac{1}{2}$

7. $1\frac{1}{4}$

8. $\frac{5}{12}$

9. $1\frac{5}{12}$

Practice 3D

1. (a) 7   (b) $6\frac{1}{2}$ (c) 16

2. (a) 24   (b) $26\frac{2}{3}$ (c) $8\frac{1}{3}$

3. (a) 49   (b) 52   (c) 45
4. (a) 40   (b) 600
5. (a) 80   (b) 900
6. (a) 8, 9   (b) 3, 600
7. (a) 9, 250   (b) 5, 20
8. (a) 350   (b) 255
9. (a) 2700   (b) 112

10. (a) $\frac{9}{10}$ (b) $\frac{3}{8}$

11. (a) $\frac{3}{4}$ (b) $\frac{5}{12}$

12. (a) $\frac{10}{11}$

13. (a) $\frac{1}{5}$

Practice 3E

1. (a) $\frac{1}{8}$ (b) $\frac{5}{18}$ (c) $\frac{3}{8}$

2. (a) $\frac{1}{5}$ (b) $\frac{2}{3}$ (c) $\frac{3}{4}$

3. (a) $\frac{1}{3}$ (b) $\frac{1}{2}$ (c) $\frac{1}{4}$

4. (a) 12   (b) $2\frac{2}{3}$ (c) 4

5. (a) 5   (b) 4   (c) 5

6. $\frac{1}{6}$ m

7. $\frac{3}{10}$

8. $\frac{3}{5}$ kg

9. $\frac{1}{6}$

10. $\frac{3}{8}$ m²

Practice 3F

1. (a) $\frac{1}{9}$ (b) $\frac{5}{18}$ (c) $\frac{3}{10}$

2. (a) $\frac{3}{20}$ (b) $\frac{1}{20}$ (c) $\frac{4}{27}$

3. (a) $\frac{2}{15}$ (b) $\frac{1}{9}$ (c) $\frac{1}{12}$

4. $\frac{2}{5}$ m

5. $\frac{1}{5}$

6. $\frac{1}{20}$ kg

7. $\frac{1}{10}$ ℓ

8. $\frac{3}{16}$ m

9. $\frac{1}{8}$ kg

Practice 3G
1. 42
2. $70
3. $180
4. 40
5. 24
6. 192

7. (a) $\frac{3}{16}$ (b) $3200

8. 46

Review A
1. (a) 515 407   (b) 4 600 000
2. (a) eight hundred and seventy-two
   thousand, five hundred and twenty
   (b) one million and thirty-four thousand
   (c) four million and five hundred thousand
   (d) one hundred and sixty-two thousand
   and three
3. 9 millions or 9 000 000
4. 5 164 000
5. (a) $438 000   (b) 43 000 km
6. 281 000
7. $2 356 000
8. (a) 1, 2, 4 or 8
   (b) 40 (or any multiple of 40)

9. (a) 5000   (b) 35 000
   (c) 3000   (d) 8000
10. 4200, 6000
11. (a) 21 000   (b) 300 000
    (c) 700   (d) 90
12. (a) 1 590 000   (b) 4 980 000
    (c) 2 752 000   (d) 16
    (e) 16 R10   (f) 12
13. (a) 1008   (b) 3900
    (c) 19 680   (d) 14
    (e) 24   (f) 12 R13
14. (a) 79   (b) 54
    (c) 22   (d) 32
    (e) 23   (f) 9
    (g) 40   (h) 9

15. (a) $\frac{3}{4}$ (b) $\frac{3}{5}$ (c) $\frac{2}{3}$ (d) $\frac{4}{5}$

16. (a) $\frac{43}{8}$ (b) $\frac{40}{11}$ (c) $\frac{41}{9}$ (d) $\frac{11}{4}$

17. (a) $3\frac{1}{3}$ (b) $4\frac{1}{2}$ (c) 11   (d) $3\frac{3}{4}$

18. (a) $\frac{6}{8}, \frac{9}{12}, \frac{12}{16}, \frac{15}{20}, \frac{18}{24}, ...$

    (b) $\frac{1}{3}, \frac{4}{12}, \frac{6}{18}, \frac{8}{24}, \frac{10}{30}, ...$

    (c) $\frac{10}{18}, \frac{15}{27}, \frac{20}{36}, \frac{25}{45}, \frac{30}{54}, ...$

    (d) $\frac{22}{28}, \frac{33}{42}, \frac{44}{56}, \frac{55}{70}, \frac{66}{84}, ...$

19. (a) $\frac{2}{3}$ (b) $\frac{5}{18}$ (c) $3\frac{1}{2}$ (d) $2\frac{6}{7}$

20. (a) $\frac{3}{2}$ (b) $2\frac{1}{2}$ (c) 4

    (d) $1\frac{6}{7}$ (e) $4\frac{2}{3}$ (f) $\frac{16}{5}$

21. (a) $1\frac{5}{8}, 1\frac{3}{4}, \frac{9}{4}, \frac{9}{2}$ (b) $1\frac{2}{8}, 1\frac{2}{3}, \frac{8}{2}, \frac{36}{5}$

22. $\frac{7}{9}$

23. 13

24. (a) $1\frac{7}{12}$ (b) $3\frac{19}{24}$ (c) $8\frac{3}{10}$

    (d) $5\frac{1}{7}$ (e) $4\frac{1}{12}$ (f) $3\frac{11}{15}$

25. (a) $1\frac{2}{5}$ (b) 15   (c) 14

    (d) $\frac{2}{3}$ (e) $\frac{7}{12}$ (f) $\frac{8}{15}$

    (g) $\frac{1}{5}$ (h) $\frac{7}{16}$ (i) $\frac{1}{21}$

26. (a) 60 cm   (b) 1 kg 700 g

27. (a) $\dfrac{1}{3}$ (b) $\dfrac{8}{15}$

28. 25
29. 354
30. 45 cm
31. $347
32. 192
33. $1120

34. $\dfrac{7}{8}$

35. $\dfrac{7}{10}$ kg

36. 18

37. $1\dfrac{1}{2}\ \ell$

38. $\dfrac{3}{20}$ kg

39. $\dfrac{1}{8}$

40. (a) $\dfrac{2}{5}$ (b) $1500

41. 2 m
42. 896

Practice 4A
1. A = 21 cm²
   B = 22 cm²
   C = 36 m²
   D = 49 m²
2. 150 cm²
3. 144 cm²
4. (a) 63 cm²   (b) 5104 m²

Practice 5A
1. (a) 1 : 2   (b) 3 : 2
2. 4 : 3
3. 7 : 3
4. 14 ℓ
5. 24 m
6. 40 kg
7. 350

Practice 5B
1. 5 : 12
2. 12 : 4 : 7
3. 4

4. 77
5. 5 : 6
6. (a) 30 cm   (b) 20 cm
7. (a) 4 m³   (b) 8 m³
8. 102 kg
9. $75

Review B
1. 19 000
2. $43 000
3. (a) 6700   (b) 72 800
   (c) 350 000   (d) 430
   (e) 580   (f) 628
4. 24

5. $\dfrac{4}{15}$

6. $\dfrac{1}{4}$

7. 2 h 15 min
8. 60 cm
9. (a) $105   (b) $80   (c) $165
10. 3 m

11. $\dfrac{1}{10}$ m

12. 48

13. $1\dfrac{1}{5}$ kg

14. 375
15. $504
16. $195
17. $45
18. $57
19. $36
20. 300 m², 70 m
21. $120
22. 9 cm², 14 cm
23. (a) 44 m, 84 m²   (b) 58 cm, 140 cm²
24. $\angle a$ = 160°
    $\angle b$ = 205°
25. (a) 207°   (b) 47°
26. (a) 75 cm²   (b) 42 cm²
    (c) 18 cm²
27. 54 m²
28. (a) 24 cm²   (b) 25 cm²
    (c) 240 cm²   (d) 10 cm²

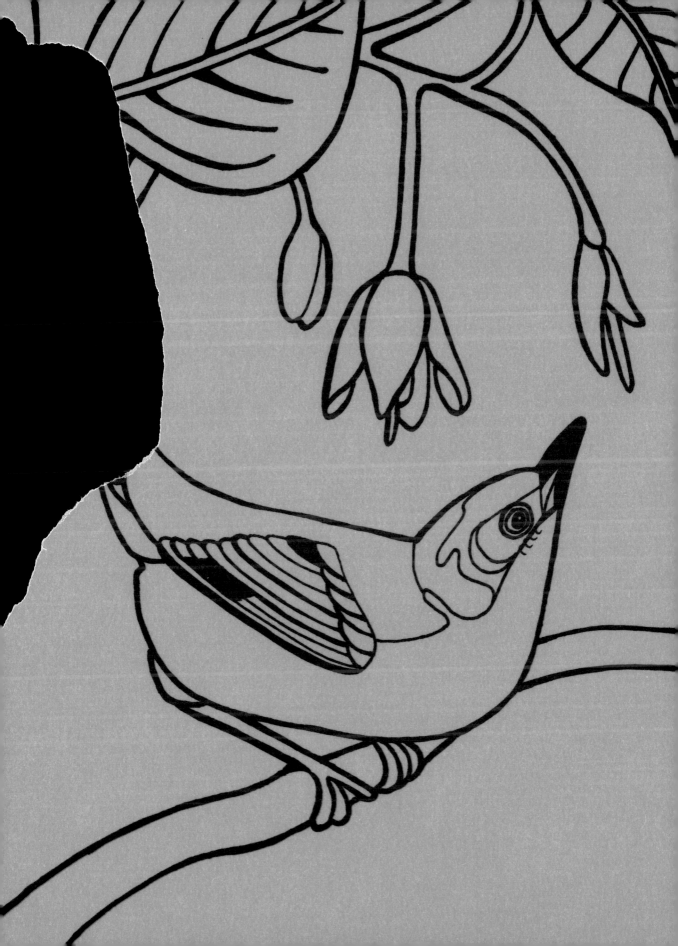

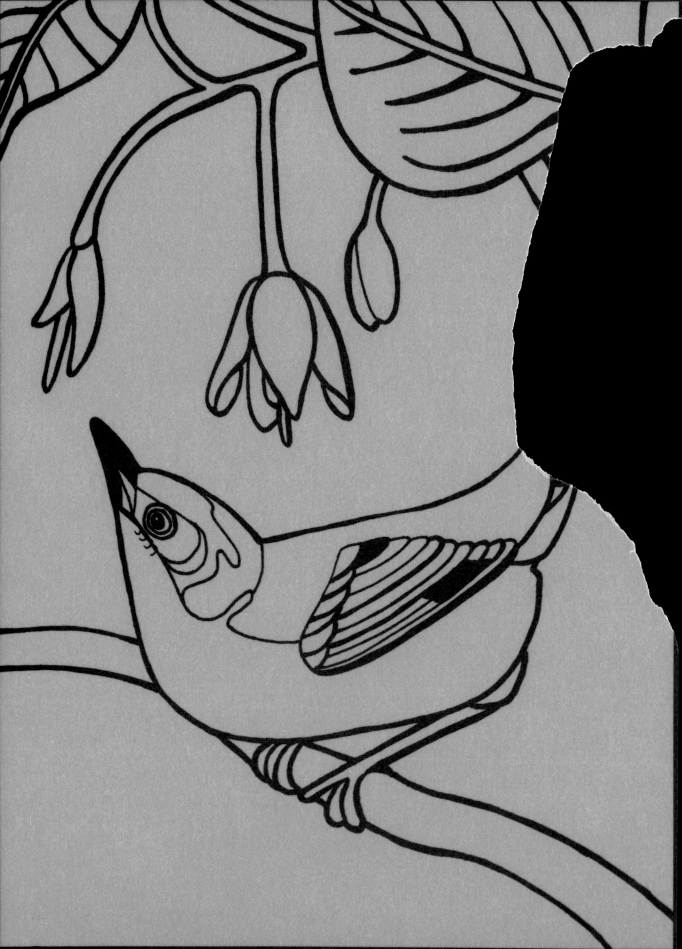